CB RADIO

CB RADIO

A Complete Guide

by

LEN BUCKWALTER

tempo books

GROSSET & DUNLAP

A FILMWAYS COMPANY

PUBLISHERS   NEW YORK

ACKNOWLEDGMENTS

For their kind assistance in providing photographs and other illustrations for this book, the author wishes to thank E. F. Johnson Co., Electronic Industries Association, REACT, Radio Shack, Fanon, Breaker, Shure Bros., Regency, Pace, and Lafayette Radio-Electronics.

ISBN: 0-448-12520-X

A Tempo Books Original
Tempo Books is registered in the U.S. Patent Office

Published simultaneously in Canada
Printed in the United States of America

CONTENTS

1. The Telephone That Goes Anywhere   *1*

2. Shopping for a CB Set   *18*

3. How to Install Your Own Equipment   *32*

4. Tuning and Maintaining Your CB Set   *40*

5. Putting Up an Antenna   *50*

6. Getting to Know CB Language   *59*

7. Translating Ten and Other Codes   *76*

8. How to Operate Your CB Radio   *86*

9. What to Do in an Emergency   *93*

10. How to Decode What Truckers Say   *99*

11. CB Rules and Regulations   *125*

1

The Telephone
That Goes Anywhere

"CB may be the fastest-growing communications medium since the Bell telephone," *Time* magazine described CB radio in September, 1975.

Plenty of statistics supported their claim. During that year one out of every fifteen cars boasted a CB radio and boat-owners were buying sets at twice that rate. More than half of all long-haul trucks on the nation's highway rode with a CB radio.

But early in 1976, FCC officials in Gettysburg, Pennsylvania, where licenses are issued, sensed a new trend. For years they had handled about 20,000 applications a month, but the numbers suddenly shot skyward. In the most spectacular performance in FCC history, licenses were pouring in at the rate of 400,000 each month. CB was putting wheels on the telephone.

One reason for CB's explosive growth is the ease with which you can get started. There is no test to take, no theory to learn, and no demand for electronic knowhow. If you can flip a switch and speak into a microphone, that is all the technical skill you need. Any member of your family, regardless of age, may work a CB set and, in fact, there is no such thing as a CB operator's license. The most official act you will perform is filling out a form for a station license and sending it to the FCC. Even the fee is modest—$4 every five years.

Another factor contributing to CB's popularity is that it is the most exciting personal toy ever dreamed up by electronic engineers. Imagine driving in downtown Los Angeles or New York with the power to communicate to a million other souls through a gadget the size of a cigar box. No wonder the CB airwaves continuously crackle with people calling home, motorists chatting along the highway, teenagers socializing, recreational vehicles choosing camp sites, pleasure boaters asking where the fish are biting, and homebodies exchanging pickle recipes.

What's more, CB is emerging as the greatest lifesaver since the seat belt. Every year more than 30 million cries for help are sounded and answered via CB radio. It is growing so rapidly as a highway aid that police departments in eight states have equipped patrol cars with sets to link into the motoring public's ballooning radio network.

Low-cost equipment, another CB attraction, can thank the solid-state revolution—the changeover from tubes to transistors. Until the 1960s, a two-way radio for an automobile was a hulking affair filled with glass tubes. It took so much room that one half the set was mounted in the trunk, another section under the dash, and the loudspeaker bolted near the driver's feet. With today's teeny electronic chips a whole CB set can fit into a glove compartment, with room left for road maps.

Fig. 1–1. Operating a mobile CB rig. (Courtesy of Radio Shack.)

As the CB radio equipment shrank, so did the price tag. In the 1970s a radio for a police or fire department cost about $1500. But the demand for CB radio and soaring production slashed these costs tenfold. In 1976 a good CB radio sold for about $150 and boasted the equivalent of hundreds of transistors.

But equipment is not the only reasonable item. When the FCC created the band in 1958, it announced a novel policy: anyone could install CB. Most two-way radios today must be installed and tested by a professional technician with a special license. Under the relaxed regulations the do-it-yourselfer can install each major section of a CB system —radio, cable, and antenna. These units are manufactured to easily hook together.

The greatest lure of CB radio, however, is communicating. You can speak from your car over a distance of about ten miles, or nearly double that distance from your home. Besides contacting your family, you can talk to scores of other stations in many areas. Thousands of volunteer monitors over the country stand ready to dispatch a police car, ambulance, or other authority in response to any emergency. If you own a boat, you may join a flotilla of CB-equipped craft and share fishing reports. In some regions you can call ahead and reserve a motel room, or find a service station to repair your car. Camp sites and mobile homes buzz with CB communication.

The Arab oil embargo of 1973 opened CB's most colorful era. As fuel supplies shortened and the national speed limit dropped to 55 mph, long-haul truck drivers snapped CB radios from dealer shelves. Through their rolling intercom they could tell each

Fig. 1–2. CBer may install his own equipment. (Courtesy of Breaker.)

other where fuel was available and flash warnings about radar speed traps. CBers eavesdropping on trucker channels were captivated by a new language —"Smokey's taking pictures," or "Headed for Shaky City with a load of four-legged Go-Go Dancers" (see Chapter 10 for translation). By 1975 CB was hailed as the "new information and entertainment radio network of the road."

Where will it end? Experts predict that CB may find its way into 80 million private cars (about the number of vehicles that now have regular car radios), most of the nation's 30 million trucks, and millions of recreational vehicles. If you want to join the fun and win CB's practical benefits, here's where to start.

Fig. 1–3. A handie-talkie carries communications any-where. (Courtesy of E. F. Johnson Co.)

The License

You won't need a license for each CB radio you own. The sets you purchase function in a system—for family or business matters—that operates under a single station license. A typical system is one mobile unit in a car, a unit for the home, and maybe one aboard a boat. The call letters that appear on your license cover all units under your control.

The person who fills out the application form becomes responsible for how the station operates. Anyone in your family or in your employ may work the sets, but the ultimate responsibility rests on the signer. The age for obtaining a license is eighteen years or older, but this could be lowered to sixteen by the time you read this. About the only group barred from a CB license is a corporation controlled by a foreign government.

You will need an FCC Form 505. Use the one supplied in this book, or, if necessary, obtain additional forms from your nearest FCC office. (See the end of this chapter.)

Another requirement is that you must have a copy of the CB rules and regulations in your possession. The current rules are printed in Chapter 11 of this book, but small changes occasionally creep in. You can learn about future changes by writing to: Superintendent of Documents, Government Printing Office, Washington, D. C. 20402. Ask for Volume VI, Part 95, FCC Rules and Regulations.

The license, once a complicated legal document, is now simplified. Even so, today's applications are bounced by the FCC because of numerous errors.

Don't forget to allow one empty box for each space between words. Here's how to avoid other errors.

Item 1.   Name

Fill this out only if the license will be in your name as an *individual*. Print clearly in capital letters, entering one letter inside each box. Use pen or typewriter, not pencil.

Item 2.   Date of Birth

Don't enter the *name* of the month. Use the number. Your birth date determines whether or not you meet the age requirement. Don't make the common error of entering the date you are filling out the form.

Item 3.   Business Name

This item remains blank in most cases because the form is filled out by an individual. Use it only to identify a business or other organization that will hold the license.

Items 4, 5, 6, and 7.   Mailing Address

This needs no explanation unless your address is a P.O. Box number. FCC officials may want to check your equipment if you commit a violation and they won't find your station at the post office. Fill out 8, 9, and 10 to show where the station is located.

Item 11.   Type of Applicant

If you want CB for private pursuits, check "Individual." If CB will aid your occupation or business and you filled in Item 1, you are still an "Individual."

When applying in the name of a business or other organization, don't mark "Individual," but the suitable category in Item 11.

Item 12.   Reason for License

Newcomers to CB should check "New License."

(When the license expires in five years, you will check "Renewal.") Ignore the request for your current call sign because you don't have one.

Item 13. Class of License

Don't use the box marked "Class C." This is a Citizens Band reserved for hobbyists who build model boats, cars, and airplanes for control by radio. Mark "Class D," the service for voice communications.

Item 14. Number of Transmitters

The term "transmitter" means any CB set or transceiver. If you are a typical applicant, mark the first box ("1 to 5") because most families have two or three sets. A business with several vehicles, on the other hand, will probably check the "6 to 15" box. You don't have to be precise—just guess. The FCC merely needs an approximate number for statistics and planning.

If you check the last box ("16 or more") your application won't be approved unless you attach an explanation. A nationwide chain of electronic stores, for example, has one license to cover thousands of demonstrator units. A fleet of trucks, too, can justify a large number of units under one application.

Items 15, 16, and 17. Signature

You will sign the application and certify that you will operate under the rules. You may not, for example, purchase equipment of excessive power, utter obscenity over the air, or play music. Don't forget to sign and date the form or it will bounce.

Because you are required to have a copy of the CB rules, the application has instructions for obtaining them from the U.S. Government Printing Office. The copy of the rules in this book satisfies that requirement as of March 1976. You should, however, keep up with later changes.

No matter where you obtained the 505 form—in this book, from an FCC field office, or inside the carton of a CB set—the application is filed at:

> Federal Communications Commission
> Gettysburg, PA 17325

Enclose a check or money order for $4 made out to Federal Communications Commission.

The licensing facility in Gettysburg is automated, but huge quantities of CB applications may delay your license. If you receive no response within two months, do not call the Gettysburg office. Instead, write to:

> Federal Communications Commission
> Washington, D.C. 20554

Don't phone. Although the FCC has lines for handling CB complaints, you will get speedier action with a letter explaining all the details. It helps trace the application.

FCC FORM 505

Addresses of FCC offices may be found
on the third and fifth pages following.

United States of America
Federal Communications Commission

Form Approved
GAO No. B-180227(R01 02)

APPLICATION FOR CLASS C OR D STATION LICENSE IN THE CITIZENS RADIO SERVICE

FCC FORM 505

December 1974

Instructions

A Use a typewriter or print clearly in capital letters. Stay within the boxes. Skip a box where a space would normally appear.

B Sign and date application.

C Enclose appropriate fee with application. DO NOT SUBMIT CASH. Make check or money order payable to Federal Communications Commission. No fee is required for an application filed by a governmental entity. For additional

fee details, including amount and exemptions, see Subpart G of Part I, FCC Rules and Regulations.

D Do not enclose order form or subscription fee for FCC Rules.

E MAIL APPLICATION TO FEDERAL COMMUNICATIONS COMMISSION, GETTYSBURG, PA. 17325.

2 Date of Birth

Month	Day	Year

1. Complete if license is for an individual

Applicant's First Name   Init.   Last

3. Complete if license is for a business

Applicant's Name of Business, Organization, Or Partnership

◀ CUT HERE

4. Mailing Address (Number and Street) If P.O. Box or RFD# Is Used Also Fill Out Items 8 –10.

5. City

6. State

7. Zip Code

8. If Item 4 is P.O. Box or RFD#, Give Address Or Location Of Principal Station

9. City

10. State

11. Type of Applicant (Check one)

- [ ] Individual
- [ ] Association
- [ ] Corporation
- [ ] Business Partnership
- [ ] Governmental Entity
- [ ] Sole Proprietor or Individual/Doing Business As
- [ ] Other (Specify) _____

12. This application is for

- [ ] New License
- [ ] Renewal
- [ ] Increase in Number of Transmitters

NOTE:
Do not operate until you have your own license Use of any call sign not your own is prohibited

IMPORTANT
Give Current Call Sign

PART 2 OF 3 PARTS

FCC FIELD OFFICES

Alabama
FCC
113 St. Joseph Street
Mobile, AL 36602
(205) 433-3581

Alaska
FCC
4th and G Street
P.O. Box 644
Anchorage, AK 99510
(907) 272-1822

California
FCC
312 North Spring Street
Los Angeles, CA 90012
(213) 688-3276

FCC
1245 Seventh Avenue
San Diego, CA 92101
(714) 293-5460

FCC
300 South Ferry Street
Terminal Island
San Pedro, CA 90731
(213) 831-9281

FCC
555 Battery Street
San Francisco, CA 94111
(415) 556-7700

Colorado
FCC
19th St. between California
& Stout Streets
Denver, CO 80202
(303) 837-4054

Washington, D. C.
FCC
1919 M Street, N.W.
Washington, D.C. 20554
(202) 632-7000

Florida
FCC
51 S.W. First Avenue
Miami, FL 33130
(305) 350-5541

FCC
500 Zack Street
Tampa, FL 33606
(813) 228-7711, Ext. 233

Georgia
FCC
235 Peachtree Street, N.E.
Atlanta, GA 30303
(404) 526-6381

FCC
Bull & State Streets
P.O. Box 8004
Savannah, GA 31402
(912) 232-4321

13 This application is for (Check only one)

☐ Class C Station License
(NON-VOICE—REMOTE CONTROL OF MODELS)

☐ Class D Station License (VOICE)

14 Indicate number of transmitters applicant will operate during the five year license period (Check one)

☐ 1 to 5   ☐ 6 to 15   ☐ 16 or more (Specify No. ☐☐☐ and attach statement justifying need.)

15 Certification   I certify that:
• The applicant is not a foreign government or a representative thereof.
• The applicant has (or has ordered from the Government Printing Office) a current copy of Part 95 of the Commission s rules governing the Citizens Radio Service
• The applicant will operate his transmitter in full compliance with the applicable law and current rules of the FCC and that his station will not be used for any purpose contrary to Federal. State. or local law or with greater power than authorized
• The applicant waives any claim against the regulatory power of the United States relative to the use of a particular frequency or the use of the medium of transmission of radio waves because of any such previous use. whether licensed or unlicensed

WILFUL FALSE STATEMENTS MADE ON THIS FORM OR AT-TACHMENTS ARE PUNISHABLE BY FINE AND IMPRISONMENT. U.S. CODE, TITLE 18, SECTION 1001.

16 _____
Signature of Individual applicant or authorized person on behalf of a governmental entity or partnership. or an officer of a corporation or association

17 Date _____

PART 3 OF 3 PARTS

Hawaii
FCC
P.O. Box 1021
Honolulu, HI 96808
(808) 546-5640

Illinois
FCC
219 South Dearborn Street
Chicago, IL 60604
(312) 353-5386

Louisiana
FCC
600 South Street
New Orleans, LA 70130
(504) 527-2094

Maryland
FCC
31 Hopkins Plaza
Baltimore, MD 21201
(301) 962-2727

Massachusetts
FCC
India & State Streets
Boston, MA 02109
(617) 223-6608

Michigan
FCC
Washington Blvd.
   & Lafayette St.
Detroit, MI 48226
(313) 226-6077

Minnesota
FCC
4th & Robert Streets
St. Paul, MN 55101
(612) 725-7819

Missouri
FCC
601 East 12th Street
Kansas City, MO 64106
(816) 374-5526

New York
FCC
111 W. Huron Street
   at Delaware Avenue
Buffalo, NY 14202
(716) 842-3216

FCC
641 Washington Street
New York, NY 10014
(212) 620-5745

Oregon
FCC
319 S.W. Pine Street
Portland, OR 97204
(503) 221-3097

Pennsylvania
FCC
2nd & Chestnut Streets
Philadelphia, PA 19106
(215) 597-4410

Puerto Rico
FCC
P.O. Box 2987
San Juan, PR 00903
(809) 722-4562

Texas
FCC
300 Willow Street
Beaumont, TX 77701
(713) 838-0271

Texas *(Continued)*
FCC
1100 Commerce Street
Dallas, TX 75202
(214) 749-3243

FCC
515 Rusk Avenue
Houston, TX 77002
(713) 226-4306

Virginia
FCC
870 North Military Highway
Norfolk, VA 23502
(703) 420-5100

Washington
FCC
909 First Avenue
Seattle, WA 98104
(206) 442-7653

2

Shopping for a CB Set

Do you want to talk from your car, home, or office? Is your CB set going aboard a boat or recreational vehicle? You will need answers to questions like these before looking at the CB models of a local dealer. CB sets fit into categories of base, mobile, combination, or portables, and you will want to choose one to match your needs. After the choice is narrowed to a basic type, you can pick a model with special features that make the set convenient, or more fun, to operate.

Shop among the wares of a reliable manufacturer. A CB radio can be an electronic jewel, and you will want to win the benefits of good engineering. Another advantage in dealing in reputable brands is service. If a dealer is connected with a responsible manufacturer, he is backed by a factory warranty and service facilities.

Junk occasionally appears in the marketplace. Reacting to an insatiable demand for CB in the mid-1970s, some manufacturers rushed to market with shoddy equipment. You will lower your chances of buying inferior merchandise by looking for the words "FCC Type Accepted." If they are missing from sales literature or the set, the manufacturer has failed to comply with federal regulations. It is illegal to market unapproved equipment, and chances are high that the quality is poor. Type acceptance is no guarantee you are getting your money's worth—but shun equipment that does not have it.

The heart of any CB system is the "transceiver." Grafted from the words "transmitter" and "receiver," that is exactly what it is: a transmitter to send your voice over the airwaves and a receiver for picking up distant voices. Both sections are built inside one cabinet. Besides saving space, a transceiver is economical because its sections share many parts.

No matter what kind of transceiver you buy, it should have most of the controls shown in Fig. 2–1. Consider what each one does.

Channel Selector. Like the one on your TV set, this control chooses the desired CB channel. If a set is capable of all-channel reception, the highest number on the selector is 23, the total number of CB channels.

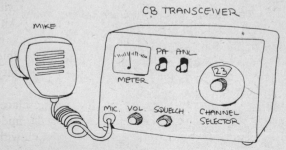

Fig. 2–1. Operating controls.

Sets with less than twenty-three channels usually mark the channel selector in letters, not numbers. A three-channel rig, for example, may show A, B, and C. The reason is that a manufacturer has no way of knowing which channels you will install. As we will see, specific channels are for certain types of operation, and channels may vary according to your location in the country. (Your dealer can tell you this information.)

The CB channel knob does more than a TV station selector. When you place the selector on "3," for example, you will receive stations on that channel. At the same time, the selector tunes the transmitter to channel 3 so you can speak to the station you are hearing. Known as *crystal-controlled tuning,* it is fast, convenient and accurate. And it is safer than older sets that had continuously variable tunable dials. You won't fumble as you drive because the selector clicks into place.

On-Off Volume. This knob is identical to the one on a regular radio. Turning it switches on the power and adjusts the loudspeaker to a comfortable level. The volume controls only incoming voices. It does not adjust your voice loudness as you speak on the radio.

Squelch. When no stations are on the channel, a stream of static and noise fills the room. It is annoying at home and disturbing in an office atmosphere. The squelch control solves the problem. When no signals arrive, the squelch automatically switches off sound to the loudspeaker. When someone calls, however, the squelch senses the signal and opens the speaker so you can hear it.

The squelch needs help from the operator—which explains why it has a knob on the front panel. You must carefully turn it until the static in the speaker *just* disappears. If the squelch is carelessly adjusted, it might silence weak stations you want to hear.

Automatic Noise Limiter (ANL). Vacuum cleaners, electric motors, and other electrical items generate static in a CB transceiver. The Automatic Noise Limiter reduces it. This device is particularly important in a car because of spark plugs, voltage regulators, and other noise-makers. In some CB sets, the ANL is called a noise blanker or noise silencer.

Although a noise limiter works automatically, it still needs a switch on the front panel. Limiters are not perfect and they distort the audio in the loudspeaker. When there is no interference, the ANL can be switched off for improving the sound.

Mike. This item is supplied as standard equipment. Mikes are plug-in parts, so you can remove them and reduce the risk of theft when you leave the car.

CB mikes operate with a push-to-talk button. To speak on the air, push the button and hold it down while you talk. Releasing the button switches the set to receive so you can hear other stations. A coil-cord is usually supplied with the mike to keep the cable from tangling.

PA (Public Address). This switch converts the CB transceiver into a miniature public address amplifier. All you need is an extra speaker to complete the PA system. (The set's built-in speaker cannot be used for PA. Because it is close to the mike, it would cause howling noises.)

The PA feature becomes a bullhorn at outdoor or sports events. For the boatman, it converts the set to a loudhailer for calling other boats across the water or directing a helper on a dock.

These features are found on CB sets in almost all

Fig. 2–2. The S/RF indicator is located near the top center of the panel.

price ranges. Next, examine the items that vary with the cost of the rig.

Indicators. There is more to operating a CB rig than talking and listening. As you communicate, you will want to know whether you are "getting out," and you will want to be able to tell a station how well he is coming into your set. This information is shown on a front-panel indicator. The most common type is the S/RF meter. *S* means strength, or the power of the station entering your receiver. Marked in units from 1 through 9, the *S*-meter provides a reading you can report to another station. "You're S5," for example. S5 is a strong signal, so the distant station is assured there is no difficulty in communications. S2, on the other hand, means the voice is nearly lost in the background noise.

The same indicator works when you speak. After you press the mike button, the meter becomes an RF (Radio Frequency) indicator. It assures that radio waves from the CB set are "getting out." If the meter falls to a low reading, it is signaling that something is wrong with the system and you are not transmitting at normal range.

Besides an S/RF meter, some sets have a *modulation indicator* to yield information about how your voice is being sent out. As you speak, a needle bounces in step with each syllable, or a light flashes. This tell-tale sign has one disadvantage; it only tells what is happening inside the set. On a deluxe CB model, however, an SWR (Standing Wave Ratio) meter tells what is happening outside the cabinet. This meter monitors the signal in the antenna system. A broken antenna rod or damage to the cable, for example, changes the SWR reading.

Another special indicator is the on-the-air sign. When you press the mike button, the sign illuminates to indicate you are transmitting. Some sets have a

Fig. 2–3. A mobile CB transceiver. (Courtesy of Regency.)

small lamp that glows when the mike button is depressed.

Once you are familiar with these CB features, decide on the type of rig you will need—base, mobile, or a combination of the two. Consider these factors.

Mobile. A mobile rig is for any vehicle that moves —the family car, truck, or boat, a farm tractor, an airplane, or a camper. Mounting space is usually limited, so a mobile rig is miniaturized. It never has tubes and is crammed with solid-state (transistorized) circuits so the rig easily fits under a car dashboard or against a boat bulkhead.

A mobile rig operates from battery power. Because there is no house current on most vehicles, the set functions from 12-volt DC, a common mobile power source.

Fig. 2–4.   A base station. (Courtesy of Fanon.)

Fig. 2–5. A base station, seen here in a living room, is highly styled. (Courtesy of Radio Shack.)

Before you purchase a mobile rig, find out if your car or boat has a positive or a negative ground. The standard is negative, and CB mobiles are designed for it. But there are rare instances of old American cars, foreign cars, and a few American trucks with a positive ground. If you are not sure, ask your auto dealer or mechanic. Many CB radios may hook to either system, but check before you buy.

Base Station. The first requirement of a base station for home, office, or other fixed location is a cord that plugs into house current. In the manufacturer's literature this is identified by words like AC, 110-volts, 115 VAC, 117 volts, or 120 VAC. They all mean the same thing: house current from a wall outlet.

Because a rig at home is usually placed on a table-top, a base station cabinet is often several times larger than that of a model designed for mobile installation. The knobs on a base rig are easier to handle because they are not jammed together. A roomier cabinet also accommodates a larger loud-speaker so audio is more pleasant to hear. Indicating meters are wider and easier to read.

Greater cabinet space also allows a manufacturer to build in more accessories, like a digital clock or extra switches that allow you to choose between two antennas.

The styling of a base station is more sumptuous than that of its mobile cousin. Because the rig appears in the home, the cabinet may look more like a hi-fi set than a two-way radio. Walnut cabinets, sleek lines, and exotic panel lighting show the designer's hand at work.

Some base stations still contain tubes instead of transistors. Tubes are not superior to transistors and, in fact, have a shorter life. But a demand in the marketplace keeps them alive. It is falsely reasoned that tubes are larger and thus more powerful, but all CB sets put out about the same transmitter power (4 watts). There is no great harm in insisting on tubes; just be sure to have them checked every two or three years.

Mobile/Base Station. Some rigs are combination or mobile/base stations. To fit a dual role, they operate from house current or a vehicle's 12-volt DC. These sets have mid-size cabinets, so check to see if there is sufficient room for mounting one in the cramped quarters of a car. The mobile/base set

Fig. 2–6. A telephone handset replaces the mike. (Courtesy of E. F. Johnson Co.)

carries a higher price tag because of its versatile power supplies.

Once you have selected a model, consider these deluxe items to improve CB operations.

Telephone Handset. CB does not work like a home telephone; one person talks at a time. To make CB function like a true telephone, the number of channels would be cut in half. Yet, the telephone handset is enjoyed by CBers willing to pay something extra. One advantage is private listening. If your CB is in an office where you want to keep others from eavesdropping or prevent being disturbed by the loudspeaker, a handset silences the rig. When you pick up the handset, the loudspeaker voice is diverted to the earpiece.

Another benefit is found in high-noise situations. Hearing a loudspeaker in a truck cab or other vehicle might be difficult. With a handset held to your ear, you shut out noise and place the desired sound almost inside your ear.

Channel 9 Priority. If you are interested in helping other CBers, you will monitor 9, the emergency channel. You will also tie up your receiver and miss calls on other channels. With a channel 9 priority you can communicate on any channel, and be warned if someone is on 9. The device automatically locks on the emergency channel whenever it is active as you monitor any other frequency.

SSB (Single SideBand). This technique transmits with much greater power than a conventional CB set. The advantage is that it has a capacity for about 30 percent greater distance and a superior ability to cut through interference.

Single sideband, on the other hand, is not widespread. It is more expensive than regular sets (about twice the cost) and you may communicate with only another SSB station. Because sideband rigs are not compatible with regular CB, the voice is garbled on

Fig. 2–7. A single sideband transceiver. (Courtesy of Pace.)

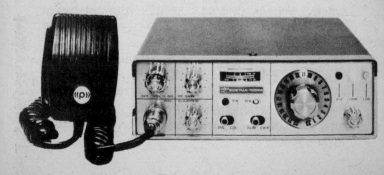

standard rigs. Sideband reception also demands careful tuning with an extra clarifier to make speech understandable.

Single sideband is not completely incompatible with regular CB. It can be used to talk to regular CB sets if a switch is turned to AM (the regular system). But in doing so, sideband loses its extra power and is as effective as any other set. Most sideband operators communicate among themselves, often on channel 16.

Handie-Talkies. The smallest mobile rig is the hand-held set that goes anywhere, thanks to built-in batteries and a telescoping antenna. Available in almost any power from 1 to 4 watts, the handie-talkie (or walkie-talkie) is a marvel of miniaturization that boasts features of the larger sets. The range of a handie-talkie is below that of other sets because of the limited antenna, but it provides communications for a small boat, a campsite, in the field, etc. Some hand-held sets convert to temporary base stations. If you remain at a campsite, you can attach a large antenna to boost the range, or save the batteries by plugging into the cigarette lighter of a car.

When you are in a dealer showroom, carefully examine a prospective CB model. Listen to voices coming over its loudspeaker. Can you turn up the volume without distorting the sound? Ample, clear audio is important from a CB set in a noisy environment.

The CB receiver should have good *sensitivity;* that is, the ability to pick up weak signals and separate them from the background noise. Many stations transmit from automobiles traveling beyond your area and you will need a sensitive receiver to work them.

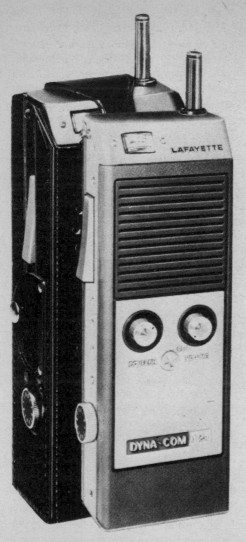

Fig. 2–8   A pair of handie-talkies. (Courtesy of Lafayette Radio-Electronics.)

Selectivity is another important quality. This is the ability of a receiver to reject interference from stations that are not on your channel. Listen to the set while tuned to channel 3, for example. Strong stations on adjacent channels 2 and 4 should not "bleed" through the loudspeaker. Good CB receivers have filters to reduce this problem. Some models add a circuit called *dual conversion,* which also cuts down interference.

You won't be able to use your new transceiver when you get it home until you acquire the second most-important piece of CB equipment. Chapter 3 will tell you how to select and mount the antenna.

How to Install
Your Own Equipment

Ordinary household tools—screwdriver, wrench, pliers and drill—handle most of a CB installation. You can do the job alone, but ask a friend to lend a hand. Many steps in the installation go much faster with an assistant. He can hold parts, pull wires, and assist in the tune-up.

Start your mobile installation by sitting in the driver's seat while a helper holds the rig in several positions under the dash. The most popular location is to the right of the steering wheel, but don't overlook other possibilities. A tiny CB set may fit in the narrow space between the door on the driver's side and the steering wheel. In this spot it won't interfere with the knees of a passenger in the center seat. A small rig may also fit in the glove compartment where it is concealed from view.

While your helper holds the set and you are in a driving position, check to see if you can reach every control. Can you conveniently grasp, then replace, the mike? If a location passes these tests, see if the set will obstruct the car's operating controls (heater, air conditioner, etc.). Feel under the dash with your fingers where you will mount the set. Are there obstructions that will block the CB mounting bolts? Turn on the heater to see if it blows hot air at the CB set. High temperature damages transistors.

When you have chosen a good spot, mount the bracket supplied with the set. Hold it in place and mark holes in the underside of the dash. Before you drill, feel under the dash and push any cables out of the way.

Before you mount the set, connect the power and antenna cables. The red and black wires from the set connect to the positive and negative sides of the car's electrical system. In most instances, the negative side is the car's electrical ground (the dashboard or any mass of metal).

The red, or positive, wire connects to a 12-volt source. Some manufacturers recommend a connection directly to the car battery because it may reduce noise from the ignition system. Many CBers, however, hook the red wire to a fuse block or accessory terminal at the back of the ignition switch. The

Fig. 3–1.   Mobile connections.

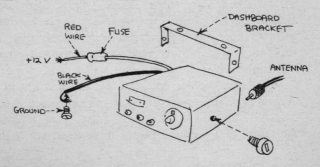

advantage of the accessory terminal is that you can operate the CB set, with the car engine on or off, and not risk burning out the car battery. The CB set shuts off when the ignition key is removed. If you don't know how to locate the accessory terminal, find the power lead to your regular car radio and follow it to the source.

Most vehicles have a negative ground, but there are exceptions. If your car has a positive ground, the red and black leads are reversed. Your rig, however, must be rated for operation on a positive ground.

After the CB set is fastened in the mounting bracket, figure out a place for the mike hanger. It is usually fastened to the left or right side of the CB cabinet. Choose the most convenient position.

The first time you turn on the rig and drive down a highway, you will be greeted by a chorus of ignition noises in the speaker. Spark plugs, alternator, and other electrical items emit radio *hash*. It disappears when you adjust the squelch knob on the receiver. Turn the knob until the speaker grows quiet —but not a fraction more. If the squelch is turned too far, the receiver won't respond to distant stations.

A squelch, however, does nothing to reduce ignition noise while a station is being received. An incoming station turns on the speaker, and ignition interference rides into the set along with the voice.

One noise-fighting tactic is the Automatic Noise Limiter (ANL) on the CB set. Switch it on when ignition noise is heavy. Although the ANL reduces the volume of the station, it often means the difference between understanding the other station or not.

Your biggest receiving problem will be hearing weak stations mixed with ignition noise. In an emergency situation where you must make contact, one way to kill the noise is to stop the car, turn off the engine, and then communicate.

There are other ways to reduce ignition noise. Because they require skill to install, check with a competent radio technician if you cannot handle the job. Some examples follow.

Spark Plugs. These are the worst noise generators, but they are easy to identify. When the plugs fire, they cause a popping noise in the loudspeaker that is exactly in step with the speed of the car engine. Pump the accelerator pedal, and the frequency of the noise will rise and fall with the speed of the engine.

The cure, which won't always work, is to clip spark plug suppressors to each plug. Another remedy is to change spark plugs to the *resistor* type.

Fig. 3–2.   Ignition noise accessories.

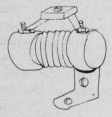

GENERATOR FILTER

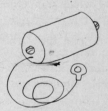

ALTERNATOR FILTER

BYPASS CAPACITOR

SPARK PLUG SUPPRESSOR

Alternator. This component produces a musical tone in the loudspeaker whose pitch rises and falls with the speed of the engine. It is helped by an alternator filter or, in bad cases, having the alternator removed and cleaned by a mechanic.

Other Points. A car's voltage regulator, windshield wiper motor, and gas gauge are also noisemakers. They are less offensive with special bypass capacitors installed by a technician.

A base station takes up little more room than a table radio, but don't plunk it down just anywhere. To keep the room free of unsightly cables, try to position the set near the window where the antenna wire enters. Check to see if there is a nearby AC outlet or whether you will need an extension cord. Any wall outlet can operate a CB because the set draws less power than most light bulbs.

The more distance between a CB and a television set, the better. A TV set sends out interference that can be picked up by the CB and sounded as a buzz or raspy noise. Separating CB and a TV, even by a few feet, can quiet the interference. Because interference will travel through a wall, avoid placing a

Fig. 3–3.   Attaching a ground wire.

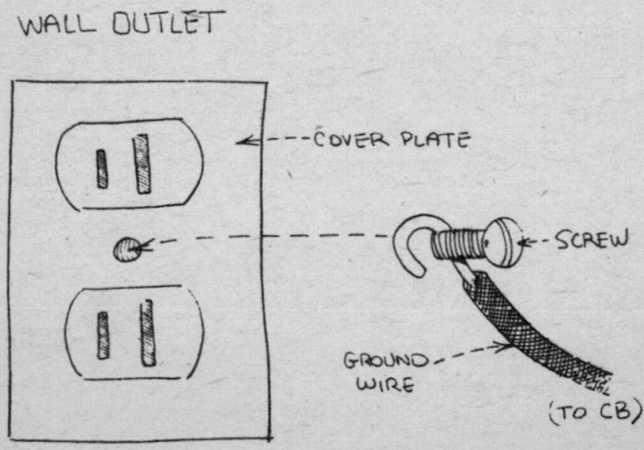

CB and a TV in different rooms, but on the same wall.

Another television problem is TVI (Television Interference). Speak into your CB microphone and you may fill the picture with wavy lines, or the TV speaker with your voice. Although this problem is helped with an accessory TVI filter (described in Chapter 4), it is easier to treat by increasing the distance between the two receivers.

Fluorescent lamps sometimes buzz in CB receivers. This problem is easy to detect by turning a lamp on and off to see if the sound changes in the CB speaker. The source is sometimes a fluorescent desk lamp, which you can move away from the CB set.

CB does not generate much heat, but transceivers are sensitive to hot spots in a room created by a heating system. Don't place a set atop a radiator or on a table pushed against a hot air duct or heating pipe. If hot air enters the cooling slots on the CB cabinet, it shortens the life of electronic parts inside.

An electrical ground aids CB operation and also improves lightning protection. A CB antenna is a target for a lightning strike, but electricity should pass

Fig. 3–4. Installing a lightning arrestor.

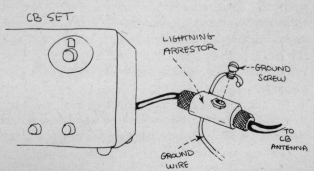

harmlessly into the earth if you provide a good electrical ground. In most homes, there is a ground at the wall outlet, where the CB set plugs in. Between the sockets you will notice a screw that holds on a wall plate. Connect a wire under the screw and run it to the ground screw on the set (which is usually at the rear of the cabinet).

Installing CB radio in a boat is usually simpler than in a car. There are more mounting possibilities because a boat is less confining than a car. Begin by finding a location for the CB, starting near the wheel or tiller. In a runabout, there is usually an open spot within reach under the instrument panel.

On larger crafts, consider the bulkhead or a shelf inside the cabin. It is handy to operate the radio while piloting a boat, but if space is limited, you can sacrifice this convenience more easily than in a car. Unlike driving an automobile, you can usually sail safely without constant attention to the area ahead. Thus you can place a marine set several feet away from the tiller and still reach the mike. Turning the CB loudspeaker to a higher volume makes up for the distance.

When you position the set, be aware of the elements. Salt spray is corrosive to electronic parts and spoils the appearance of the cabinet. Protect the set from the weather and don't leave it outside at the end of the boating day. When you are under way and the sea is rough, figure some way to waterproof or protect the set. A plastic bag works as a temporary measure.

Always purchase an antenna designed for marine use. Most boats are fiber glass or wood—materials that cannot form an electrical ground for launching the CB signal. There is plenty of metal in a car body for grounding, but a boat antenna must create its own electrical ground. Besides, marine CB antennas are usually made of fiber glass for greater resistance to salt and weather.

Whether you have an outboard or larger craft, ignition noise is often troublesome when you are under way. Engine manufacturers are aware of the problem and offer special kits for treating it. Ask your marine dealer about them. If you cannot completely suppress noises, remember that you can stop the engine and communicate if there is an emergency.

In most boats, the CB antenna is the tallest structure, which makes it a tempting target for lightning. Strikes are rare, but it is not difficult to convert the antenna to a lightning rod and discharge the bolt into the water. Join the boat's metal areas—engine, radio, rudder, rails, etc.—with heavy copper wire (size No. 8). To complete the path into the water, one of those metal parts (at least one foot square) must lie below the water line. If there is none, have a ground plate fastened to the hull and follow the manufacturer's instructions.

The final touch to a marine installation is obtaining CB crystals for channel 13 (if your rig is not an all-channel type). This is where most pleasure boaters talk and where you will find other sea-going CBers ready to communicate with your new rig.

4

Tuning and Maintaining Your CB Set

Colorful cards hanging from the display rack of your dealer include the gadgets of CB accessories. After you have been on the air a month, you will wonder if these items can squeeze more distance from your station or make it easier to operate. Some are showy gimmicks, like a sign that lights and says you are on the air, but many are useful replacements—plugs, cords, switches, for original parts that break or wear out.

Many CB accessories are not only worth their price, but they keep paying for themselves. Some reduce interference that ruins communications or disrupts TV reception. Other accessories make your station more convenient to operate, or keep it in good repair. Here's a sampling of major items and what they offer.

Connected to a CB set, the wattmeter reads transmitter power. Its accuracy is much greater than a spoken report like, "Your signal is weak today." Because CB radio is limited to only 4 watts, a wattmeter tells if the transmitter is working properly. You should see a reading between 3 and 4 watts.

A wattmeter also localizes trouble. Let's say you are not transmitting far enough, but have no inkling where the problem lies. Hook the wattmeter to the set and take a reading. If the power measures over 3, it means the transmitter is functioning. If it is less, look for trouble beyond the transmitter with the next accessory.

The SWR meter is also valuable. Every CB antenna has *standing waves*—surges of current that flow from transmitter to antenna. In a perfect CB system, each wave flowing to the antenna is absorbed. But if there is a broken wire, or a damaged antenna element, part of the wave bounces back to the transmitter. If you compare the forward wave with the reflected flow, you will have a good idea of how the antenna is working. This is the function of an SWR meter. It measures Standing Wave Ratio or SWR. In a perfect system, it would read "1 to 1" but practically speaking, any reading under 1.3 to 1 means the system is in good condition. Measurements above that figure suggest the antenna system needs checking.

An SWR meter is especially valuable for mobile antennas. Because car bodies come in different shapes, an antenna manufacturer often includes an adjustment to electrically match the antenna to your vehicle. This is done by changing the length of the antenna tip. You will know when the length is correct by watching the SWR meter; it drops to the lowest reading.

Another useful indicator, the field strength meter is placed several feet from the CB antenna. As you transmit, it acts as a miniature receiver that picks up

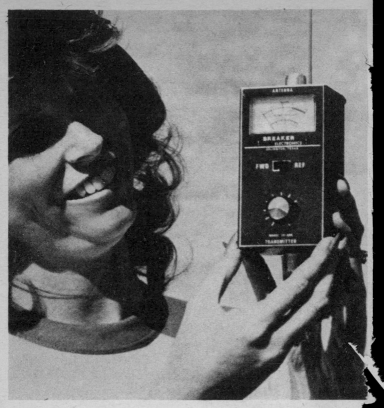

Fig. 4–1. SWR meter. (Courtesy of Breaker.)

your signal and displays it on a meter. It is an excellent companion to the instruments mentioned above because it provides a valuable cross-check; the field strength meter and wattmeter read highest, while SWR is lowest.

The dummy load is an inexpensive gadget that plugs into the antenna socket of your CB rig and turns the power into heat. This is valuable when you measure your rig with a wattmeter or SWR instrument because it keeps your signal off the air. The law, in fact, says you should create as little interference on the air as possible while testing. The dummy load helps you meet the requirement.

Two dummy loads are available. One is a small lamp that glows with power; the other resembles an antenna plug. The latter, which contains a resistance element, is more accurate for exact power measurements.

An antenna matcher squeezes efficiency from a mobile antenna. Placed in the line to the antenna, it

Fig. 4–2.   Antenna matcher. (Courtesy of Radio Shack.)

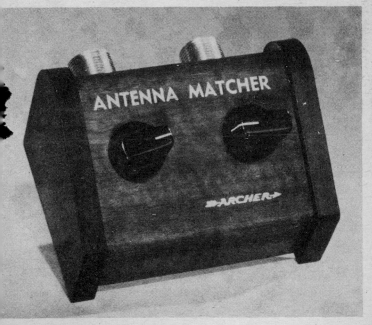

tunes out the mismatch that creeps into the system. Two adjustments on the instrument are varied until you read the lowest SWR on a meter connected in the antenna line. Have someone turn on the CB transmitter while you tune the matcher.

The antenna switch saves time when there is more than one connection to the CB set. You may for example have two antennas and want to choose between them. Instead of disconnecting and attaching cables to the set, you can flick the antenna switch for an instant changeover.

The switch is also handy for making a quick check of your CB transmitter. Connect an antenna to one position on the switch and a test meter on another position. When you suspect something is wrong, you can rapidly turn the switch to the tester and check the power.

The microphone supplied with your CB rig works well for most situations. It is designed for close-talking—your lips should almost brush against the case. Speaking this close excludes traffic and road noises.

Close-talking may not be convenient at home or in the office. With a cluttered desk or table it is handier to place the CB set and mike several feet away from you. To avoid reaching for the mike each time you speak, you can use a power mike and talk at a distance. The mike has a built-in amplifier that boosts your voice. You don't have to bring the mike to your mouth for each transmission; merely press a talk bar on the microphone.

A power mike works best in a home or office with a quiet atmosphere. Because it is highly sensitive, the mike picks up too much noise in a mobile installation.

Fig. 4–3.   Power mike. Note the push-to-talk bar on the base. (Courtesy of Shure Bros.)

It takes special skill to install a power mike. Unless you are competent in this area, ask your dealer about the job. It consists of buying a mike connector to match the one on the CB set, and then wiring it to the power mike.

Any television set may suffer TVI (Television Interference) from a nearby CB set. The symptoms are seen on the screen or heard in the loudspeaker. Wavy lines fill the picture, the picture reverses (light areas become dark), or unusual colors fill the screen. You will suspect the CB set because the interference jumps in step with your voice. In some cases, the voice is also heard in the loudspeaker—garbled on some channels, remarkably clear on others.

There are several ways to fight TVI. One is to keep the CB antennas as far as possible from the TV

Fig. 4–4.   A TVI Filter on the back of a TV set.

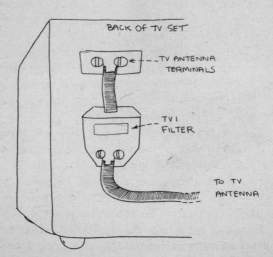

antenna. Distance weakens the interference. Another method requires an accessory attached to the CB set. Known as a *low-pass filter,* it prevents the interfering signal from reaching the CB antenna. There is also an accessory you can install on the television set. Called a *high-pass filter,* it connects to the TV antenna terminals and blocks CB interference.

You won't always be within hearing distance of your CB set. While working outdoors or in a garage, you may miss an incoming call. An accessory that carries the call to you is an extension speaker. Many CB sets have a socket at the rear to divert the sound to an external speaker. You can also run a long line to a speaker outside. For outdoor use, consider a model that is resistant to weather.

Another convenience with an extension speaker is using it as a boat loudhailer. The CB set must have a built-in PA (Public Address) feature that allows you to speak into the mike and have the audio sent to an external speaker. It is helpful to hail a helper ashore when you are leaving or returning to a dock or beach, or to speak to passing boats.

Many accessories, like the meters described above, signal a warning when something is wrong. But before you pull the set from the car dash or take it to a service technician, look for troubles you can fix yourself.

Consider a dead set. Many times this is nothing more than the result of the plug not being inserted into a wall outlet. A similar trouble occurs in a mobile rig when a passenger pokes a foot under the dash and snags the power lead. The wire pulls out and removes the power. To avoid this nuisance, tape wires from the set under the dashboard. You will find plenty of other cables to serve as anchor points.

Check for a blown fuse. In a rig operating on house current, the fuse is often located inside a cartridge at the back of the set. Remove the plug from the wall outlet, then examine the fuse. Fuses occasionally blow for no apparent reason, so insert a new one. If it blows, too, this is a good sign that the rig should go to the repair shop.

If a second fuse does not blow, it was probably a case of metal fatigue—the original fuse simply retired. Sometimes the fuse in a mobile rig, mounted in the power cable, does not make good electrical contact. Clean the contact area with a rough cloth and try again.

No modulation (meaning there is a carrier signal, but your voice is missing) is often caused by a broken microphone cable. After you have grabbed the microphone several hundred times, the wires flex and break. It happens most often at one end of the cables—where it enters the microphone or where it plugs into the set. Your dealer can furnish a replacement. If you don't know how to resolder connections to the cord, have it done by a serviceman.

Antenna cables also cause problems, often at the coaxial connectors, where the cable attaches to the antenna. After months of operation, moisture creeps into the connector and causes corrosion. Remove and clean any connector located outdoors, and then retighten it. A coating with black plastic tape is good protection against further attack from the elements.

If your trouble lies deep within the CB transceiver, take it to a technician who specializes in two-way radio repair. To work on certain sections of the transmitter requires an FCC Commercial Radiotelephone license which, most local radio-TV repair shops do not have. Most major CB manufacturers have factory authorized service centers listed in your owner's manual. If there is none near you, write to the manufacturer and ask if you can obtain service at the factory. CB sets are small, and it is sometimes practical to mail them to the factory for repair. Before you pack the set, however, carefully check the items mentioned before. You will want to be certain the problem is inside the CB transceiver before sending it out for repair.

5

---

*Putting Up
an Antenna*

No other item of your CB system is open to more choices than the antenna. An antenna is a collection of aluminum tubes that resembles anything from a shiny spire to the remains of a fish. And there are more mounting styles than you would find at a riding academy. So let's look at several popular antenna installations and see how they wring the most signal from your CB rig.

The most powerful antenna for a car is a nine-foot shaft in the center of the car roof. It would be a fabulous performer—until you tried to park in a garage or pull into a car wash. At nine feet, the antenna smashes overhead lights and twangs against the ceiling. If you drive down a tree-lined street, it clips low-lying branches. A nine-footer is electrically excellent but a mechanical nightmare.

To keep the mobile antenna manageable, manufacturers offer the *loaded whip*. Loading is done with a small coil, seen as a bulge somewhere along the length of the rod, which makes the antenna seem like nine feet to the transmitter, but at a shorter physical length. Too much loading, though, wastes power. A rule-of-thumb is that the shorter the antenna, the shorter will be your communicating range. A one-foot antenna heavily loaded with a coil, for example, would be a poor choice. Most mobile whips are three to four feet long.

Another difference is where the manufacturer puts the loading coil; at the top, bottom, or center. The best communicating range is from a top-loaded coil because it pulls the most power up the antenna. But you won't see a coil at the very tip because the antenna becomes too top heavy. A top coil also causes your voice to fade in and out as the antenna sways. For this reason, coils are often placed somewhere between the middle and top of the antenna.

Other models place the coil at the base. This is a good location for mechanical strength and there is little sway as you move over the road. Some models add a spring at the base to absorb shock if the antenna strikes an overhead object.

You won't see the coil on the popular mobile antenna known as a *continuously loaded whip*. Concealed inside a shaft of fiber glass, the coil follows a spiral from bottom to top.

Which is the best mobile antenna? Although performance improves as a whip grows longer and is mounted higher on the vehicle, you can get excellent results with almost any conventional design in the three-to-five-foot length. Performance also depends on where you put it.

There are about a half-dozen places on a car to mount a mobile antenna. A popular position is on the trunk deck, behind the back window, on the left or right fender. Placing it on a rear fender is an excellent idea because the antenna is at a high point with few obstructions. A disadvantage to some people is the need for a small hole drilled into the car body. This was once considered harmful to a car's resale value, but CB's popularity has probably eliminated this objection.

The trunk-lip antenna is an extremely popular design because it requires no holes and is easy to install. A clamp fits in the groove of the trunk lid and passes the wire into the car body. The clamp holds the antenna erect, but does not interfere with opening and closing the trunk.

Despite the towering height, the nine-foot whip is chosen by some CBers but it must be attached on the rear bumper to avoid striking obstacles. Although the antenna is partly obstructed by the car body, this is usually offset by the antenna's great length

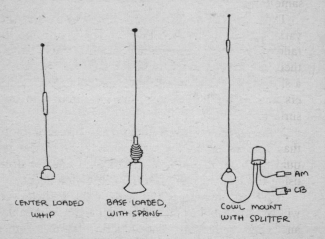

CENTER LOADED WHIP   BASE LOADED, WITH SPRING   COWL MOUNT WITH SPLITTER

Fig. 5-1   Mobile antennas.

and efficiency. A bumper mount, incidentally, is a good solution for vehicles without a metal roof—a jeep, for example.

There are several options for an antenna known as the *cowl mount,* which goes up front where the regular car antenna is located. If your present car antenna is on the right side, you can place a CB antenna on the left side. Be sure you can find a path from the antenna into the passenger compartment before you buy a cowl mount. It may take skill to fish the cable through the fender in some cars.

An attractive alternative is the CB-AM antenna, a two-in-one design. You can remove the regular car radio antenna from the front cowl and install a CB antenna in its place. Instead of one cable from the antenna, there are two: one plugs into the CB set, the other into the car radio. It comes with a *splitter,* which enables one antenna to feed both radios at the same time.

Those are the major mobile models. You will see variations at your dealer's, but these are mostly tailored for a special mounting. For the truck-owner, there are special brackets that clamp an antenna to a side-view mirror, or versatile mountings for campers and motor homes to fasten an antenna to any surface.

You can mount a mobile antenna with little more than a screwdriver and wrenches. If the model requires a hole, it can be made with an electric drill, using the hole size given in the instruction sheet.

After an antenna is fastened to the vehicle you will run the cable to the CB set. You can buy cables and plugs separately, but soldering them together is a tricky, tedious job. It is simpler to purchase a cable assembly that has the hardware already attached to the cable. If the antenna is to be mounted on the rear deck of the car, a twenty-foot cable assembly should take care of almost any run. The cable is attached to the bottom of the antenna inside the trunk, then fished under the back seat into the passenger compartment. Hide the wire under the carpet or behind the metal strips that run below the car doors. Loosening the strips a bit gives enough clearance for the cable. Once the cable is attached to the CB set, use a bit of tape to keep any excess from dropping on the brake or accelerator pedals, or tangling with your feet.

Antennas for home, office or other fixed stations are much larger than mobile models. Because they don't have to withstand the stress and strain of mobile operation, they may reach many feet into the air without striking obstructions.

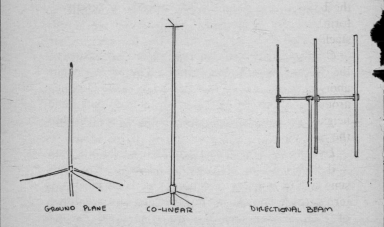

GROUND PLANE   CO-LINEAR   DIRECTIONAL BEAM

Fig. 5–2.   Base station antennas.

Base antennas are often advertised by dB gain, a power rating (in decibels) that describes how many times the antenna multiplies power from the transmitter. The antenna does not actually multiply power, but compresses it into a desired direction. The part of the radio signal that is wasted in an upward direction, for example, is squeezed into the horizontal direction, where distant stations lie.

Manufacturers advertise gain figures to prove the superiority of one model over another but, generally speaking, small differences in dB don't mean much. In each antenna category, comparable models of reputable manufacturers deliver about the same performance. Let's look at the basic types you will see on the marketplace.

Ground Plane. One of the earliest CB antennas, the ground plane survives because it is simple and low in price. It has a nine-foot shaft with several drooping rods, known as *radials,* protruding from the bottom. The ground plane turns in a good performance if it is mounted high and is clear of obstacles.

Co-linear. One of the most popular base antennas, the co-linear is taller than a ground plane. It extends about eighteen feet up and has small radial elements around the bottom. Because of added metal and height, the antenna generates strong signals toward the horizon.

Directional Type. All antennas—mobile and base —described so far are omnidirectional, that is, they send signals in every direction. This is an ideal pattern because you can work other stations, regardless of where they are located.

Another type antenna, known as a *beam,* is directional; it sends out and receives signals in a narrow direction. The advantage of a directional antenna is the great distance it can reach. Power is multiplied by concentrating it in one direction, much as a flashlight focuses light into a narrow beam. Because a beam antenna must be aimed at a narrow area, it requires a rotator motor to swing it in the desired direction. A beam's disadvantage is that you may point it west and miss a station calling from an easterly direction. The beam has poor pickup in all but one direction.

Some operators overcome the problem by installing two antennas: a conventional (omnidirectional) model for monitoring, and a beam to improve the power after communications begin.

The higher, the better, is good advice for CB antennas, but the rules prescribe limits. You could erect an antenna so high that it becomes a hazard to aircraft. There are 12,000 airports in the U.S. and you are probably near at least one. To avoid the staggering job of checking every CB antenna, the FCC imposes two general rules:

Omnidirectional Antennas. These include mobile and base antennas, used by nearly everyone, that transmit and receive in all directions. For these types, the rule is you cannot exceed sixty feet above ground level measured to the tip of the antenna. Say you live in a two-story home with a roof twenty-five feet above the lot and want to put up a twenty-foot antenna. Adding the two dimensions yields forty-five feet—you will not exceed the legal height.

You may place an omnidirectional antenna on a pole, tower or mast. Such supports were once outlawed but today they are acceptable so long as the antenna does not exceed sixty feet above ground.

Directional Antennas. Height restrictions are tighter for the directional antenna: a beam or other type that sends a stronger signal in one direction than in others. To keep your station from interfering with too many other CBers, the law limits these powerful antennas to twenty feet above a man-made structure or natural formation. Notice nothing is said about ground level. This rule relates to the supporting point for the antenna, usually a roof or a chimney. You may not put a beam antenna atop a mast or tower.

Survey your roof for a spot to mount the antenna. The location should be high and as far from obstacles as possible. Your antenna won't perform efficiently if it is less than about ten feet from nearby masses of metal like power lines and rain gutters. Fortunately, the brackets, straps and hardware for TV antennas also work well for CB. Strapping the CB antenna to a chimney, for example, is easily done with a TV chimney mount. There are wall and pipe brackets for almost any other mounting possibility.

When you have picked a location, begin the job by assembling the antenna on the ground. It is safer than juggling aluminum tubes while balancing yourself on a roof. When the antenna is together, have a helper hand it to you, or hoist it with a rope to the rooftop.

You will be wary of falling off the roof, but there is another hazard—electrical wires. Never handle an antenna in a way that would allow it to contact electrical cables in the roof area. If the antenna slips from your grasp, it should never be able to brush against those wires.

When the antenna is in place, connect the antenna cable at the bottom. You will have good results over the years if you wrap the antenna connector with black plastic tape to keep out water and corrosion. Run the cable down the building and through a groove or other opening in the window frame to the CB set. To secure the cable against flapping in the wind, use TV stand-offs to support wire along the way.

Getting to Know
CB Language

Tune across the CB band and you will hear a babel of jabberwocky and slang. You may guess the meaning of "to eyeball," or solve one like "landline," but many terms—barefoot, bleed, and 88s—defy ordinary translation. To help you solve this problem, this chapter includes a dictionary of CB technical talk and lingo that covers almost any cryptic term you will hear in the air, including your "handle."

As your unofficial CB name, rank, and serial number you will use a handle more than your call sign or real name. There is no legal objection so long as you use your call letters at the beginning and end of all communication.

Choose a handle carefully because it says more about you than your real name. Four Stroke and Speed Demon have obvious roots, while Mr. No-One and Sinker cry for self-confidence. Peach Cake and Pussy Cat are lovable (what else)?

To help you choose a handle, here are dozens of actual examples heard on the airwaves. Look them

over, then dream up one that communicates your
best—or worst—trait.

A	Bud Man
Adam-12	Buffalo Bill
Apache	Buffalo Soldier
Arabian	Bulldog
Augie Doggie	Bumble Bee
	Busy Bee

B	
Barbie Doll	C
Barkin' Bone	Calamity Jane
Barracuda	Candy Kitten
Bat Man	Candy Man
Beacon Kid	Canuk
Beaver	Captain Fantastic
Beefeater	Cardinal
Beer Can	Carpenter
Big Bad Bob	Cat Nip
Big Ben	Cattle Man
Big Blue	CB Seven
Big Daddy	Challenger
Big Eddy	Charlie Brown
Big Red	Chili Coyote
Black Bart	China Clipper
Black Falcon	Chocolate Chip
Blacksmith	Cisco Kid
Blue Aster	Clipper
Blue Bill	Cold Beer
Blue Bird	Country Boy
Blue Eagle	Cowboy
Blue Jay	Coyote
Blue Shark	Cricket
Bruno	Cucumber

D
Daddy-Long-Legs
Diamond Red
Dirty Dan
Doggie-Doggie
Doggy Daddy
007
Dragon Lady
Droopy Drawers

E
Early Bird
Easy Rider
Elmo

F
Fender Bender
Flintstone
Flipper
Free Bee
Fresno Wolfman
Four Stroke
Fuzzy Bear
Fuzzy Cat

G
Gas House
Gear Jammer
Golden Ace
Golden Hawk
Golf Man
Grand Slam
Granny
Grave Digger
Green Eyes

Green Hornet
Ground Hog
Grumpy Turtle
Gutter Ball

H
Half Pint
Hercules
Hi-Flier
Hill Billy Bear
Hindenburg
Honey Comb
Hotpoint
Hot Poker
Hot-Shot
Hot Rock
Hurricane

I
Iron Man

J
Jaguar
Jamaica Man
Jaws
Johnny Reb
Jumpin' Jack
Junior Whopper

L
Lead Penny
Little Honda
Little John
Lucky Lady
Lumberjack

M

Mad Dog
Maiden Marion
Maltese Falcon
Mean Persuader
Middle Man
Minny Mouse
Mister Clean
Money Man
Monty Python
Moon Man
Moose Man
Mouse Whiskers
Mr. Big Stuff
Mr. No-one
Mudslinger
Muskrat
Mush Mouth

N

Night Crawler
Night Hawk
Night Raider
Nomad

O

Oceanview
Ol' Cotton Picker
Old Bird

P

Panama Bandit
Peach Cake
Penguin
Pistol Pete

Polar Bear
Polliwog
Pony Tail
Professor
Proud Pappa
Puddy Cat
Purple Chicken

R

Razor Red
Rebel
Red Baron
Red Devil
Red Dog
Red Rider
Red Snapper
Red Wing
Renegade
Rockin' Chair Hippie
Rocky Road
Rolling Cat
Rubber Ducky
Rubberneck

S

Safecracker
Salty
Sardine
Scout
Scout Master
Screaming Demon
Shady Lady
Shake N' Bake
Sherlock Holmes
Shoe Fly

Silver Bullet
Silver Fox
Silver Streak
Sinker
Sky Diver
Skylark
Sleep Walker
Slim Jim
Soul Patrol
Snake Eyes
Snoopy
Snowbird
Snuff-skceter
Speed Demon
Speedy
Spitfire
Sugar Cookie
Sun Burst
Super Ducky
Super Goose
Swamp Fox
Sweat Hog
Sweetheart
Sweet Mama
Swivelhips

T
Tater Gal
Tea Totaler
Texas Ranger
The Flash
The Raven
Thin Man

Tight Wad
Timber Wolf
"T. J."
Tony the Tiger
Tough Stuff
Troublemaker
Trouble Shooter

U
Uncle "J"

V
Velvet Voice
Viking

W
Wacky Wheels
Waterdog
Watoosie
Weatherman
White Dog
White Ghost
White Shark
Whiskey Sour
Wild Cat
Wild Fire
Wolfman
Wrench Bender

Y
Yellow Bird
Yellow Jacket

Next, you will want to understand the special expressions heard almost exclusively on the CB band.

Affirmative	Yes
Barefoot	A CB rig without an illegal power booster
Base rig	CB transceiver at home, office, or other fixed location
Beam	Powerful, highly directional antenna
Big Daddy	Federal Communications Commission
Big switch	On-off knob on CB set
Bleed-over	Interference from station on the next channel (one higher or one lower)
Bootlegger	Operator without a license, or one who uses a false call sign
Breaker	Operator who wishes to join conversation in progress or to start a new one
Clear	Message complete
Coffee break	Social meeting of local CBers
Come again, or **Come on**	Answer me
Covered up	Blanked out by another station
Definitely	Maybe
88s	Love and kisses
Eyeball	To meet another CBer in person
Fox Charlie Charlie	FCC, or Federal Communications Commission
Getting out	Transmitting well
Ham	Amateur radio operator

Handle	Nickname used on the air
Home 20	Town where you live
Jamboree	Special event sponsored by CB club consisting of social activity and equipment display
Landline	Telephone
Lid	Awkward operator
Linear	An illegal power-boosting amplifier
Mercy, or Mercy Sakes	Conversational pause, takes the place of "um"
Mike	Microphone
Mobile rig	CB transceiver installed in automobile
Negatory	Negative, no
OM	Old man (applied to any age)
One-eyed monster	Television set
Out	Conversation is over and no reply is expected
Over	Go ahead and speak
Part 95	FCC rules governing Citizens Band
Part 15	FCC rules covering unlicensed handie-talkies
Portable rig	CB transceiver with self-contained antenna and battery pack for use in the field
Pull switches	Turn off and close down a station
QSL	Colorful postcard mailed to another operator to confirm a contact. Often displayed and called "wallpaper"
Reading the mail	Eavesdropping on other stations

Rig	CB transceiver; mobile rig, base rig, portable rig, etc.
Rock	The crystal installed in a CB transceiver to control transmitting and receiving channels, so called because it is cut from natural quartz
Roger	Message received and acknowledged
Say again	Repeat your last transmission
73	Best regards (a friendly sign-off)
Shack	Room where CB radio is located
Shout	To call another CBer on the air
Shout 'em down	Look for another station on the band
Skip	Long-distance transmission, usually more than several hundred miles, caused by atmospheric conditions
Sky hook	Any antenna
Slider	Illegal accessory that replaces crystals to control CB transmitter frequencies; also known as a VFO (Variable Frequency Oscillator), the slider is less accurate than a crystal
Stand by	Wait
Stepped on	Receiving interference from another station

Fig. 6–1. "That's a negatory, Mush Mouth. I couldn't eyeball Ol' Cotton Picker." (Courtesy of E. F. Johnson Co.)

Tennessee Valley Indians	Nickname for TVI, or television interference, caused by a CB set
That's a copy	Message received
Twenty	Short form of 10-20, the Ten Code for location
Uncle Charlie	FCC
Wallpaper	(See QSL)
Wheels	Mobile installation
Wilco	Will comply with your request
XYL	CBer's wife (Letters stand for Ex-Young Lady)
YL	Young Lady

Tech Talk

Remember when a neighbor bought the first hi-fi on the block? There was talk of "tweeter," "woofer," and "frequency response" because hi-fi is not only a pleasure to hear, but it is fun to talk about. And so is CB—if you learn the electronic vocabulary. Here are the key terms.

Technical Term	*Definition*
AC	Alternating Current, the type found in most homes
AGC	Automatic Gain Control. In the CB receiver it keeps loudspeaker volume constant on strong and weak stations

AM	Amplitude Modulation. The CB system for putting a voice on a radio wave
Amperes	Unit of electrical current
ANL	Automatic Noise Limiter. Accessory on a CB transceiver to lower interference from a car ignition and other electrically-noisy sources
Band	A group of frequencies or channels. CB is in the 27 MHz band
Base station	Transceiver, usually large in size, at a fixed location operating from house current
Beam	Highly directional antenna, usually aimed by a rotator motor
Carrier	The radio wave that carries the voice
Channel	Specific spot or frequency within the CB band
Clarifier	Control knob on single sideband sets. A clarifier makes the incoming voice intelligible
Class D	The most popular CB band, on 27 MHz. Other bands are little-used Class A, and Class C for controlling models by radio
Coax	Pronounced "co-ax," it is the shielded cable that connects the CB set to the antenna
Coaxial Cable	Line from the CB transceiver to the antenna

Technical Term	*Definition*
Crystal	Device that tunes the CB receiver and transmitter to an exact frequency or channel
DC	Direct Current, the type of power in a battery or vehicle. Voltage is usually 12
Decibel (dB)	Comparison between two power levels. Mostly used to rate antenna performance
Delta tune	Knob on CB transceiver for fine-tuning stations transmitting slightly off-channel
Dual conversion	Receiver circuit for cutting out interference from stations on nearby channels
Dummy load	An attachment to a transmitter for turning the radio wave into heat. Prevents on-the-air interference while testing
11-meter band	Another name for the Citizens Band. (Also the length of a CB radio wave)
FET	Field Effect Transistor. Transistor used in CB receivers of good quality
Field strength meter	Instrument that measures the strength of a CB signal. Useful for tuning up
Frequency synthesis	Circuit in CB transceiver to reduce number of crystals for all-channel reception

Technical Term	*Definition*
Fuse block	Group of fuses mounted below the dash of an automobile. Often used as a supply point for powering a CB set
Gain	An increase in power
Ground	Connection to earth, or the common wiring connection on a CB chassis
Ground plane	Nondirectional antenna for home or base station. It has one vertical and several radial rods emerging from the bottom
Handset	Combined microphone and earphone, held like a telephone
Handie-talkie	CB set for portable operation. It has built-in antenna and batteries. Also called "walkie-talkie"
IC	Integrated Circuit. Tiny chip containing thousands of transistors. ICs may comprise several sections of a CB transceiver
Impedance	Amount of opposition to a flow of current. Each basic item of a CB system—transceiver, coaxial cable, and antenna—have an impedance of 52 ohms. This allows them to connect together for a perfect electrical match

Technical Term	*Definition*
Jack	Socket for microphone or speaker plug
LED	Light-Emitting Diode. Cold light source used for indicator lamps on the front panel. It often forms digital read-out for channel number
Linear	Illegal amplifier to boost CB power
Loaded whip	Mobile antenna shortened by a (loading) coil
Loading coil	Coil that reduces antenna below conventional size. It is most often used to lower a nine-foot mobile antenna to three or four feet
MHz	Megahertz. Measure of how many times the CB radio wave vibrates each second. Mega is one million, Hertz (named after a radio pioneer) is cycles per second. CB is on 27 MHz, meaning its wave vibrates 27 million times per second
Microvolt	One millionth of one volt. Used to measure the strength of a CB signal in the antenna system
Mike	Microphone. Converts tiny currents of air generated by the voice into electrical currents

Technical Term	Definition
Mobile rig	Transceiver powered by 12 volts for a car or other vehicle
Modulating	Speaking into the CB mike, causing the carrier, or radio wave, to vary with the voice
Noise Blanker	Similar to Automatic Noise Limiter, but more expensive and effective
Ohm	Unit of electrical resistance
Omnidirectional	Sending a signal in every direction; also termed nondirectional
Output/Power	Number of watts generated by a CB transmitter. For most sets, the limit is 4 watts
PEP	Peak Envelope Power. Method for measuring the power of a single sideband (SSB) transmitter
PLL	Phase Lock Loop. Circuit in CB transceiver that derives many channel frequencies from few crystals
PTT	Push-To-Talk. Switch on a microphone to control the transmitter. Pressing the switch turns on the transmitter, releasing the switch turns on the receiver
Quarter Wave Antenna	Basic antenna, about nine feet long, used for mobile operation

Technical Term	*Definition*
RF	Radio Frequency. Electrical wave that vibrates sufficiently fast to create radio signals. CB is in the 27 MHz band, where RF vibrates 27 million times per second
Rig	CB set or transceiver
Selectivity	Ability of CB receiver to cut off interfering stations
Sensitivity	Ability of CB receiver to amplify weak, distant stations and make them audible in the loudspeaker
Shielded Cable	Cable with an inner wire encircled by an outer metal braid or shield. Used for CB antenna and microphone cables
Signal	Radio wave from a CB station
Signal strength	Strength of incoming signal, usually indicated on S-meter
Skip	Long-distance transmission of CB signals
S-Meter	Indicator on CB set to measure strength of incoming signal
Squelch	Control that silences the loudspeaker when there is no incoming station
Squelch	Control on front panel of a CB transceiver to eliminate noise in the loudspeaker when no signal is received

Technical Term	*Definition*
SSB	Single Sideband. An efficient method of CB transmission. It is limited by high cost and complex equipment
SWR	Standing Wave Ratio. Comparison between forward reflected power in CB antenna system
Traffic	Messages
Transceiver	Basic CB radio, a combination transmitter and receiver
Transistor	Tiny, solid device that performs each basic electronic step in communications. It amplifies weak signals, generates radio waves of high frequency, or separates signals of different type, e.g. audio and radio
TVI	Television Interference from a CB transmitter
Volt	Unit of electrical pressure
VOX	Voice-Operated Transmitter. Accessory that turns on a transmitter when a voice strikes the microphone. It allows hands-free operation of the CB set
Watt	Unit of electrical power
Whip	Vertical rod for mobile antenna

7

_____

Translating Ten and Other Codes

TV actor Broderick Crawford probably started the craze when millions of viewers watched him bark "10–4" into a mike. Now this phrase is uttered by millions of ordinary citizens every day on CB. Ten Codes efficiently squeeze complete sentences into a few digits, but there is no denying that they also lend a ring of authority to the speaker's voice.

The Ten Code is not official—it was originally developed for police, and then borrowed by CBers. It has grown so popular, though, that even the code has a code. Take the most famous code of all—"10–4," which means "OK," or an agreement with the last message. You can also say, "That's a four," or plain "Four." For hearty agreement, you will hear "That's a big fat 10–4!"

"What's your 10–20?" is probably the second most common code. This asks your geographic location—a town, a neighborhood, or a stretch of highway. Besides saving time, Ten Codes get through static and interference.

Fig. 7–1. "Signals are 10-2, but if you don't stop 10-11, I'll go 10-7, 10-4?" (Courtesy of Electronic Industries Association.)

Each code works two ways. You can state it directly—"You're 10–2," meaning that someone's signals are strong—or pose it as a question—"Is that a 10–2?"—which is asking if your signals are strong.

Here is a version of the police code in general CB use.*

10 Code	Definition
10–1	Receiving poorly
10–2	Receiving well
10–3	Stop transmitting
10–4	OK, message received
10–5	Relay message
10–6	Busy, stand by
10–7	Out of service, leaving air
10–8	In service, subject to call
10–9	Repeat message
10–10	Transmission completed, standing by
10–11	Talking too rapidly
10–12	Visitors present
10–13	Advise weather/road conditions
10–16	Make pickup at _____
10–17	Urgent business
10–18	Anything for us?
10–19	Nothing for you, return to base
10–20	My location is _____
10–21	Call by telephone
10–22	Report in person to _____
10–23	Stand by
10–24	Completed last assignment

---

* Note that some Ten Code numbers have been left open so that additions may be made as they become part of the code.

10 Code   Definition

10 Code	Definition
10–25	Can you contact _____?
10–26	Disregard last information
10–27	I am moving to channel _____
10–28	Identify your station
10–29	Time is up for contact
10–30	Does not conform to FCC rules
10–32	I will give you a radio check
10–33	**EMERGENCY TRAFFIC AT THIS STATION**
10–34	Trouble at this station, help needed
10–35	Confidential information
10–36	Correct time is _____
10–37	Wrecker needed at _____
10–38	Ambulance needed at _____
10–39	Your message delivered
10–41	Please tune to channel
10–42	Traffic accident at _____
10–43	Traffic tieup at _____
10–44	I have a message for you (Or _____)
10–45	All units within range please report
10–50	Break channel _____
10–60	What is next message number?
10–62	Unable to copy, use phone
10–63	Net directed to _____
10–64	Net clear
10–65	Awaiting your next message/assignment
10–67	All units comply
10–70	Fire at _____
10–71	Proceed with transmission in sequence
10–73	Speed trap at _____
10–75	You are causing interference
10–77	Negative contact
10–81	Reserve hotel room for _____

10 Code	Definition
10–82	Reserve room for _____
10–84	My telephone number is _____
10–85	My address is _____
10–89	Radio repairman needed at _____
10–90	I have TVI
10–91	Talk closer to mike
10–92	Your transmitter is out of adjustment
10–93	Check my frequency on this channel
10–94	Please give me a long count
10–95	Transmit dead carrier for 5 seconds
10–99	Mission completed, all units secure
10–200	Police needed at _____

In the mid-1970s an organization of police officers called APCO (Associated Public Safety Communications Officers) streamlined the code and suggested it as a standard for the country. They called it the "Brevity Code Ten Signals" because signals are reduced to about three dozen and are easier to memorize. You will see that it does not always agree with the longer code given above, but most are similar.

Official APCO Signals

10 Code	Definition
10–1	Signal weak
10–2	Signal good
10–3	Stop transmitting
10–4	Affirmative (OK)
10–5	Relay (to)
10–6	Busy
10–7	Out of service

Fig. 7–2. A portable CB and clip on antenna in an attache case could be used in a rented car. (Courtesy of E. F. Johnson Co.)

10 Code	Definition
10–8	In service
10–9	Say again
10–10	Negative
10–11	On duty
10–12	Stand by (Stop)
10–13	Existing conditions
10–14	Message/information
10–15	Message delivered
10–16	Reply to message
10–17	Enroute
10–18	Urgent
10–19	(In) contact
10–20	Location
10–21	Call _____ by phone
10–22	Disregard
10–23	Arrived at scene
10–24	Assignment completed
10–25	Report to (Meet)
10–26	Estimated arrival time
10–27	License/permit information
10–28	Ownership information
10–29	Records check
10–30	Danger/caution
10–31	Pick up
10–32	Units needed, specify/number/type
10–33	Help me quick
10–34	Time

Official Radio Alphabet

No matter how clearly you speak over a radio some sounds are easily confused. Words that begin with *C* and *V, S,* and *F,* for example, or words of similar sound, like phone and foam are difficult to recognize over the air. Your listener must often identify a sound by its position in the sentence or the context. But try to communicate exact information, like a name or street sign, and it may sound garbled after several attempts.

The confusion clears with the international phonetics. Widely used in government, aviation, and marine communications, it substitutes an easy-to-understand word for each letter. Some words in the alphabet, for example, whiskey, kilo, zulu, and India, have an exotic ring, but this is intentional. They are meant to be understood by people throughout the world to whom English is a second language.

In the alphabet that follows, each letter is shown with a pronunciation guide. Accent the capitalized letters and notice that some words, YOU-nee-form (uniform) and Keh-BECK (Quebec), are sounded slightly differently from general usage.

Letter	Phonetic	Pronounciation
A	Alfa	AL-fah
B	Bravo	BRAH-voh
C	Charlie	CHAR-lee (or SHAR-lee)
D	Delta	DEL-tah
E	Echo	ECK-oh
F	Foxtrot	FOKS-trot
G	Golf	GOLF
H	Hotel	HOH-tel
I	India	IN-dee-ah
J	Juliet	JEW-lee-ett
K	Kilo	KEY-loh
L	Lima	LEE-mah

M	Mike	MIKE
N	November	No-VEM-ber
O	Oscar	OSS-cah
P	Papa	PAH-pah
Q	Quebec	Keh-BECK
R	Romeo	ROW-me-oh
S	Sierra	See-AIR-rah
T	Tango	TANG-go
U	Uniform	YOU-nee-form
		(or OO-nee-form)
V	Victor	VIK-tah
W	Whiskey	WISS-key
X	X-ray	ECKS-ray
Y	Yankee	YANK-key
Z	Zulu	ZOO-loo

It appears impossible to confuse 5 and 9, or the words five and nine, but that's on paper. Over the air they're easily mixed up. It is also difficult to distinguish between for and four over the air. This is solved by distorting the way you say the number, or by giving it special emphasis. Here is the international system. Notice that 4 and 9 have extra syllables.

Numeral	Pronunciation
1	Wun
2	Too
3	Tree
4	Fo-wer
5	Fife
6	Six
7	Sev-en
8	Ait
9	Nin-er
0	Zero

If you are telling someone a lengthy number—an address or phone number—avoid lumping numerals. The street address 2549 Maple should not be said as "twenty-five forty-nine." It is clearer to the listener if you say "too fife fo-wer nin-er." Perhaps the street name Maple could be heard as Maypole. If there is a chance for error, say the word phonetically: "Mike Alpha Papa Lima Echo."

Q Signals are three-letter combinations—QRT, QSY, etc. Like the Ten Codes, each represents a thought or sentence. Although *Q* signals are important in military and amateur radio communications, they occasionally slip into CB. Here are a few you might hear.

Q Signal	*Definition*
QSO	Contact or communication
QRN	Interference (static) from natural sources
QRM	Interference from man-made sources
QRT	Stop operating, close station
QRX	Wait
QSY	Change to a different channel
QSB	Signal fading
QSL	Post card which confirms communication
QTH	Location

Ten codes, phonetics, and *Q* signals are the spoken shorthand of radio communications. To sound like a true CBer, though, there is more lingo to sling—along with Speed Demon, Polliwog, and other denizens of the Citizens Band. Chapter 9 gives a healthy sampling.

How to Operate
Your CB Radio

Wait . . . don't touch that dial. Before you roam the airwaves, spend a few minutes perfecting your microphone technique. It profoundly affects how clearly and how far your voice travels. Place two identical rigs side by side and the operator with proper technique may reach twice as far as one who casually picks up the mike and talks. Here's how to refine your mike technique.

Newcomers to CB usually speak too far from the mike. This is understandable because professional singers and speakers often talk several inches from their mikes. A CB mike, however, is designed for close-talking. Hold it no more than an inch or two away and speak with your lips almost touching the grille.

If you speak directly into the grille, your voice might produce popping sounds. This can be avoided by holding the mike at a slight angle away from the lips. An excellent way to perfect your mike technique is to have a friend listen over the air while you experiment with different mike positions and distances.

Another mistake is speaking too rapidly. Radio talk is not the same as living-room conversation because your signals must penetrate interference and noise. A listener misses fewer words if your talking speed is slightly below normal conversational rate. If he does not hear you clearly, never raise your voice or shout. It worsens conditions by creating *splatter,* which distorts the voice and interferes with other stations.

Next, turn the selector and choose a CB channel. Out of twenty-three channels assigned to the band, you can freely use any one except 9 and 11. Channel 9 is the emergency and road-assistance frequency. As described in the next chapter, it is set aside for the safety of life, immediate protection of property, and assistance for motorists.

Channel 11 is the national calling frequency. It overcomes the problem of finding another station when the channels are busy. If the other station leaves its receiver on channel 11 all the time, it will hear your call on the channel. Once you have established contact, you will find an open channel somewhere else on the band and move there to conduct your business. Because it takes only a few seconds to establish contact on 11, the channel remains relatively clear of interference.

None of the remaining CB channels has an official purpose, so you may talk on any one. But CBers reserve channels for specific activity and you should know them. A good example is the trucker channels. When long-haul drivers installed CB in great numbers, they operated on channel 10 east of the Mississippi, and on channel 19 west of the Mississippi. Channel 10, however, created interference problems

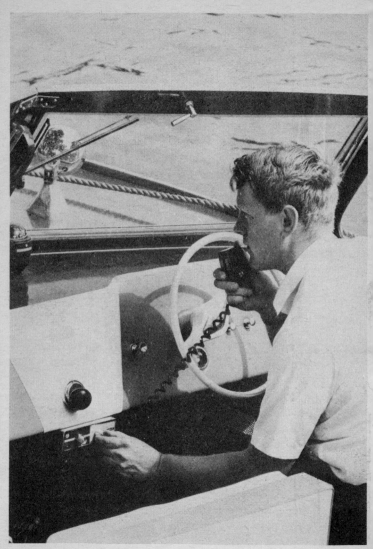

Fig. 8–1.   CB aboard a small boat. (Courtesy of Amphenol.)

Fig. 8–2.   CB in a recreational vehicle. Note the antenna above open door. (Courtesy of E. F. Johnson Co.)

to 9, the emergency channel. To solve this, the trend has been toward channel 19 throughout the country. A moment's search of the channels should locate trucker activity in your area.

Another important channel is 13, where pleasure boaters operate. If you live near a coast, the Great Lakes, or any area of small boats, channel 13 teems with nautical activity. You will learn where the fish are biting, conditions of wind and water, and who is in trouble or running out of gas.

Listen in on a channel before you press the mike button. CB is a party line and everyone has a right to use any frequency. It is a matter of courtesy (and the rules) to avoid interfering with another station. Don't worry about interfering with faint stations on the channel that barely move your S-meter. They are probably more than twenty miles away and out of communicating range. You will put weak signals into their area and cause no significant interference.

When radio conditions are right, you will hear CB operators at amazing distances. Their accents may be different from yours, but they sound strong enough to be next door. The cause is *skip,* a phenomenon that bounces signals through the upper air (iono-sphere) and returns them to earth hundreds or thousands of miles away. Skip conditions follow an eleven-year sunspot cycle. When the number of spots reached a low point in 1975, there was little CB skipping. For the following five or six years, how-ever, the cycle will increase sunspots and improve long-range skipping. The next low will be in the mid-1980s.

After listening to your set for a while, you will know how to manage your own communications. Assign a name to each unit of your station; Base refers to a fixed station at home or office; Mobile 1 could be a car; Mobile 2 a camper, truck, or other vehicle. Portable 1 may be a handie-talkie.

Operate all your units under one call sign, the letters assigned to you by the FCC. Let's say your station identification is KRU-1000 and you want to "raise" a member of your family who is driving a car:

You: This is KRU-1000, Base to Mobile 1, over.

Mobile: This is Mobile 1, over.

That's a formal procedure you can relax this way:

You: KRU-1000, the Peanut Whistle, looking for Big Horn, c'mon.

Mobile: Big Horn right back at you.

Those nicknames called—"handles"—are acceptable so long as you include the regular call sign at the beginning and end of the conversation.

Let's say you want to contact a station you don't know, or want to communicate with anyone:

You: Breaker one two, this is KRU-1000, the Peanut Whistle, go ahead.

"Break" means you want an answer from anyone listening. It can also mean you want to break into conversation existing between two stations. Wait for one station to stop speaking, then utter a fast "break-break" before the second station responds. In many instances, you will be heard and be invited to speak.

Notice the numbers in the call "Breaker *one two*," which mean channel 12. They are not really necessary because only another station on channel 12 would hear you. Numbers, incidentally, should be spoken one digit at a time. For example, 3724 is not spoken as "thirty-seven twenty-four," but "three-seven-two-four." Don't say your call letters during each give and take. So long as you identify your station at the beginning and end of the conversation, you will satisfy the rules.

There are two rules about silent periods. If you are talking to your own unit—a station with your call letters—the only restriction is that you talk for the "minimum practicable time." While in contact with another station (different call letters), your exchange may not last longer than five consecutive minutes. Beyond that period you are required to observe a one-minute silent period before talking again to that station. This gives others a chance to use the channel.

There are few other restrictions. Never play music over the air, whistle, make unusual noises, or utter obscene remarks. For safety's sake, don't operate at home or office during a thunderstorm. You can use CB for just about any personal or business activity so long as it does not violate the law.

After a couple of successful contacts with your new CB station you are ready for the codes, lingo, and special jargon that fill the airwaves.

What to Do
in an Emergency

No matter how you say it—"Mayday," "SOS," "Help," or "This is an emergency"—your call for assistance will probably be heard on CB radio. About five million such cries go out every year. Some are triggered by great natural disasters—earthquakes in southern California, hurricanes along the Gulf Coast, and tornadoes of the Midwest. But most cries for help are personal emergencies. A million highway accidents a year are reported to authorities via CB radio. Somewhere, two stranded motorists are refueled or repaired every second. Weather conditions, route instructions, and motel reservations are an arm's reach away with CB radio.

CB officially became a highway aid in 1970. Before that time, shouts of help were lost in a clutter of interfering voices. There was no emergency channel. Responding to pressure from volunteer groups, the FCC reversed an earlier policy and cleared channel 9 for messages that concern the immediate safety of life or the protection of property. At the same

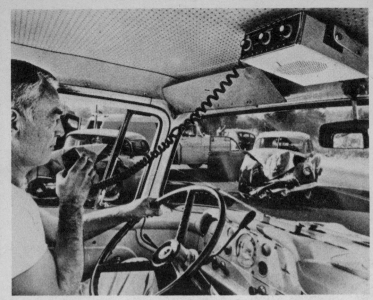

Fig. 9–1.   Reporting an accident via CB radio. (Courtesy of E. F. Johnson Co.)

time, channel 9 was reserved for routine communications to assist the traveler.

CB's success on the highway can thank volunteer operators. The U.S. Coast Guard is bound by law to listen for distress calls on the water, and Air Traffic Control guards the aircraft band for emergency calls, but in CB, these services are provided by Good Samaritans monitoring channel 9. They will receive your message and relay it by radio or telephone to police, fire, civil defense, wrecker, or other authority.

The largest volunteer organization is REACT (Radio Emergency Associated Citizens Teams). About a quarter-million CBers have banded together into 1,000 local teams to provide almost continuous coverage of channel 9. To summon a REACT station, use any wording you wish, but the following is a procedure that saves time.

Calls on channel 9 are for: (1) emergencies or (2) motorist assistance. The emergency always takes priority and is identified by saying "10–33." If you forget the numbers say "Mayday," "This is an emergency," "Help," or any other word that describes the situation. The "10–33," however, quickly alerts a monitor that someone is in immediate danger. For

Fig. 9–2. REACT monitor reporting an emergency. (Courtesy of REACT.)

Fig. 9–3.   Service station responding to a call on Channel 9. (Courtesy of Electronic Industries Association.)

example, a car ahead of you is weaving down the road, it swerves, glances off a telephone pole, and crashes into a ditch.

You might say: "This is KRU-1000 mobile calling REACT with a 10–33."

When you have made contact, tell the monitor the precise accident location. It may sound foolish to say city and *state* because CB is short range, but skip could launch your signal hundreds of miles to a town with an identical name.

An accident, especially one with injured people, is an unnerving experience. Try to remain calm as you give the details to a REACT member or other monitor. For example:

You: The vehicle hit a telephone pole. One person appears unconscious. I can't tell how badly he is injured. The car is completely off the road and is not blocking traffic in either direction. Gasoline spilled on the roadway could be a hazard.

You have given as many details as possible. Now the monitor can alert the proper authorities.

Be sure your message has immediacy and danger before transmitting on channel 9. Don't use the channel to report that traffic is flowing smoothly or you are out of gas in your driveway.

The other class of call—motorist assistance—also goes over channel 9. You may request road service to get your car operating, fuel for an empty gas tank, or give reports of stalled cars and accidents. You can also call on 9 if you are lost in unfamiliar territory. Questions like "What's the best route?" or "How do I get to Elm Street?" are acceptable. If a motel in the area has CB, you can make a reservation.

If you call a REACT monitor for road instructions say the code "10–46." For example: "This is KRU-1000 calling REACT with a 10–46."

The listener instantly knows it is not a grave emergency and you need motorist assistance.

Don't confuse channel 9 with 11, the other channel set aside for special use. If you merely want to meet another station use 11, the national calling channel. Because continuous monitoring is done only on channel 9, a distress call on channel 11 may be missed, or picked up by a station untrained in emergencies.

The ultimate method for summoning help was revealed in an experimental project by the Missouri State Highway Patrol. In the early 1970s the state set up a direct CB-to-police hookup. Operating under the call sign KMO-0911, 700 patrol cars monitored channel 9 for emergency calls. In a one-month period officers received more than 6,000 calls for assistance and reports of dangerous road conditions. CBers reported 1,540 stranded motorists and 1,002 traffic accidents. The experiment also resulted in 455 arrests and 387 warnings for drunk driving, speeding, and felonies.

At least a half-dozen other states have CB in police vehicles—Arizona, California, Connecticut, Texas, Oklahoma, and Kansas. The idea has worked so well that national coverage could be routine before 1980.

Use any channel (and any words) to call for assistance on CB. Anything goes in an emergency. State your problem clearly and completely on channel 9 and help should be on the way in minutes.

10

How to Decode
What Truckers Say

"Bear biting" does not mean an outbreak of rabies in Yosemite. A "Tijuana Taxi" is not a public conveyance in Mexico. And "reefer" is not a Turkish import. At least not if these terms are heard on CB Channel 19. These terms are from the daffy, delightful lexicon of the long-haul trucker. Here's how to translate hundreds of sassy phrases and snappy comebacks that fly over the trucker channels.

Term	Meaning
Advertising	Police car flashing lights
Anchored modulator	Operating from a base or field station
Back	Back to you
Back door	Last truck in a line moving as a group
Back door closed	Last truck protecting a line (warns against police overtaking the line)

Term	Meaning
Back down	Slow down
Back off the hammer	Slow down
Back out	Stop transmitting
Background	Interference
Backslide	Return trip
Backstroke	Return trip
Bagging	Police stopping vehicles driving over speed limit
Bang a U-ee	U-turn
Barefoot	Operating without an illegal amplifier
Barley pop	Beer
Barn	Garage
Basement	Channel 1
Bay City	San Francisco
Bean store	Restaurant
Bean town	Boston
Bear	Police officer
Bear bait	Vehicle not equipped with a CB rig
Bear bite	Speeding ticket
Bear cage	Police station
Bear cave	Police station
Bear food	Vehicle not equipped with a CB rig
Bear in the air	Police aircraft
Bear in the sky	Police aircraft
Bear meat	Vehicle not equipped with a CB rig
Beat the bushes	Drive ahead of a group, slightly over the speed limit, to lure police into view
Beaver	Female

Term	Meaning
Beer City	Milwaukee
Bending my windows	Strong signal being received
Big A	Amarillo or Atlanta
Big brother	Police
Big D	Dallas
Big M	Memphis
Big orange	Snyder truck
Big skip land	Heaven
Big switch	Switch that turns off the CB set
Big T	Tucson
Big 10–4	Hearty agreement
Bikini state	Florida
Bird	Thunderbird (Ford)
Bit on the britches	Speeding ticket received
Black and whites	Police
Bleeding	Interference from another channel
Blew my door off	Passed me rapidly
Blinkin' winkin'	School bus
Blood box	Ambulance
Bodacious	Sending a strong signal
Boob toob	TV
Boogie man	State police
Bootleg	Steal a call sign
Bottle popper	Beverage truck
Boulevard	Expressway or highway
Bounce around	Next trip through
Bouncing cardboard	Driver's license
Box	CB set
Break	Request to communicate on channel

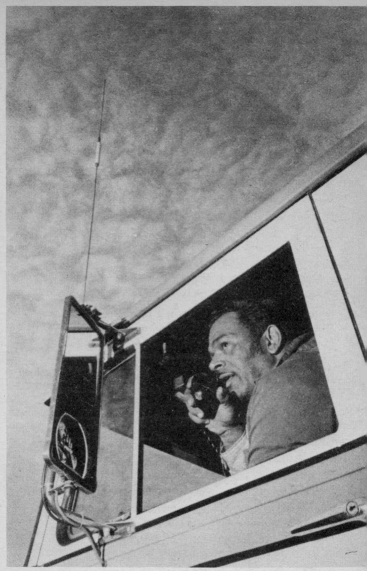

Fig. 10–1.   Trucker talking on his CB mike. (Courtesy of David A. Vine.)

Term	Meaning
Break Break	Request to communicate on channel
Breaker	Interrupting station
Breaking the needle	High reading on a CB S-meter
Breaking up	Voice becoming lost in noise
Brown bottles	Beer
Brown paper bag	Unmarked police car
Brush your teeth and comb your hair	Warning, radar ahead
Bubble machine	Flashing lights on police vehicle
Bubble trouble	Tire problem
Bucket mouth	Excessive talker
Bucket of bolts	Tractor trailer
Bullet lane	Passing lane
Bull rack	Vehicle for transporting animals
Camera	Police radar
Candy man	Federal Communications Commission
Catch	Speak to
Catch car	Pursuit car of police radar team
Charlie	Yes
Chase car	(see Catch car)
Check the seatcovers	Check the passengers (usually means female passengers)
Checking my eyelids for pin holes	Growing sleepy
Chicken coop	Weigh station
Chicken coop is clean	Weigh station is closed

Term	Meaning
Chicken inspector	Weigh station inspector
Choo Choo town	Chattanooga
Christmas Card	Ticket for speeding
Cigar city	Tampa
Circle city	Indianapolis
City kitty	Town police
Clean	No police
Clear	Final transmission
Coke stop	Rest room
Come again	Repeat your last message
Comeback	Answer to a call
Come here	Invitation to transmit
Come on	Invitation to transmit
Copying the mail	Eavesdropping on other stations
Country Cadillac	Tractor trailer
Country Joe	Country police
County mountie	Sheriff's deputy
Coupon	Ticket for speeding
Covered up	Blocked by interference
Cowboy Cadillac	Ford Ranchero
Cow town	Fort Worth
Cuda	Barracuda (Plymouth)
Cut loose	Turn off the CB set
Cut some Zs	Sleep
Cut the coax	Shut down CB set
Dead pedal	Slow-moving vehicle
Dig you out	Understand
Dog house	Engine cover
Doing the five-five	Moving at 55 mph
DOT Man	Official from U.S. Department of Transportation

Term	Meaning
Double nickel	55 miles per hour
Down and gone	Ending transmission
Down and on the side	Ending transmission, continuing to listen
Draggin' wagon	Wrecker
Dress for sale	Prostitute
Drop the hammer down	Press accelerator to floor
Dropping it off the shoulder	Running off the side of highway
Dummy	Unoccupied police car
DX	Distance (meaning radar range)
Ears	CB Radio
Eighteen wheeler	Tractor trailer
Eights and other good numbers	Love and kisses, best wishes
Eighty-eights (88s)	Love and kisses
Electric teeth	Radar
Evel Knievel Smokey	Motorcycle cop
Everybody is walking the dog	Channels are mostly occupied
Eyeball	Meet in person
Eye in the sky	Police aircraft
Fat load	Overweight truck
Fed	Federal officer
Feed the bears	Receive a speeding ticket
$50 lane	Left, or passing, lane

Term	Meaning
Final	Final transmission
Fish	Barracuda (Plymouth)
Fix	Location
Flag waver	Highway repair crewman
Flag waver taxi	Highway repair truck
Flaps down	Slow down
Flip-flop	Return trip
Flip-flopping bears	Police changing direction
Flipper	Return trip
Flop it	Turn around
Fluff stuff	Snow
Foot in the carburetor	Police are in pursuit
Foot warmer	Illegal amplifier
Four lane parking lot	Interstate highway
Four-legged go-go dancers	Pigs
Four Roger	OK, received
Four wheeler	Automobile
Fox hunt	FCC officials searching for illegal CB operators
Front door	First vehicle in a line
Funny books	Porno publications
Get horizontal	Lie down and go to sleep
Get truckin'	Accumulate many road miles
Getting out	Putting out a good signal
Girlie bear	Female police officer
Give me a shout	Answer me
Go breaker	Invitation to speak
Go-go girls	Pigs for market
Go juice	Truck fuel

Term	Meaning
Gone permanently 10–7	Died
Good buddy	General greeting
Good numbers	73s and 88s, which mean "best regards" and "love and kisses"
Good shot	No police or hazards ahead
Got a copy?	Can you hear me?
Got his shoes on	Maximum speed
Got my foot in it	Pressing on accelerator
Got your ears on?	CB turned on?
Green stamps	Money, usually for speeding ticket
Green stamp lane	Left, or passing, lane
Green stamp road	Road with toll booth
Haircut palace	Overpass or bridge with little clearance
Hammer	Accelerator pedal
Hammer down	Speed up
Hammer off	Slow down
Hammer on	Accelerate
Hammer up	Slow down
Handle	Nickname
Hang a left	Turn left
Hang a right	Turn right
Hang it in your ear	(An) answer to a foolish remark
Have a safe and sound one	Drive carefully
Hiding in the grass	Police on median strip
High gear	Illegal power amplifier

Term	*Meaning*
Holding on to your mud flaps	Follow closely
Hole in the wall	Tunnel
Holler	Call
Home twenty	Home location (10–20)
Honey wagon	Beer truck
Horse	Mustang (Ford)
Hot stuff	Cup of coffee
Jamboree	Social CB gathering
Jaw jacking	Talking
Kiddie car	School bus
Knuckle buster	Fight
Knock the slack out	Accelerate
Kodak	Radar set
Kodiak with a kodak	Police with radar
Lady bear	Female police officer
Land line	Telephone
Linear amplifier	Illegal amplifier to boost power
Little bear	Local cop
Load of postholes	Empty truck
Load of rocks	Bricks
Load of sticks	Lumber
Local yokel	City or town policeman
Make a trip	Switch to another channel
Mayday	Distress signal
Meat wagon	Ambulance
Mercy	(Speech pause for example, "um")

Term	Meaning
Mile marker	Milepost on highway
Mobile eyeball	Examine another truck while in motion
Modulate	Talk
Monster lane	Inside, or passing, lane
Motion lotion	Fuel
Nap trap	Place to sleep
Negative copy	Cannot hear
Negatory	No, Negative
Nightcrawlers	Many police in area
One time	Short contact
On the by	Listening, not talking
On the peg	Speed limit
On the side	Listening
Open season	Many police
Over shoulder	Behind, or in back of
Paper hanger	Cop giving a speeding ticket
Pass the numbers	Sign-off (see 73 and 88)
Peanut butter in the ears	Operator not listening to CB
Pickum-up	Pickup truck
Picture box	Radar set
Picture-taker	Police radar
Picture taking	Police checking speed with radar
Pigeon	Vehicle stopped for speeding
Piggy bank	Toll booth
Plain brown (or other color) wrapper	Unmarked police car

Term	Meaning
Portable barnyard	Cattle truck
Raise	To contact someone via CB
Read	Hear (How do you "read" me?)
Reefer	Refrigerated truck
Rig	CB transceiver
Road jockey	Truck driver
Rock	Crystal for CB set
Roger	Message received
Salt shaker	Cinder truck
Seat cover	Woman passenger
Set of doubles	Tractor-trailer
Shaky city	Los Angeles
Seventy-three (73)	Best regards
Shakyside	California (refers to earthquakes)
Shanty shaker	Drive of mobile home
Short short	Soon
Shout	Call
Shoveling coal	Speeding up
Sidedoor	Left, or passing, lane
Sitting in the saddle	Middle truck of three-vehicle line
Sitting under the leaves	Concealed police car
Skating rink	Slippery road
Slammer	Prison
Smile and comb your hair	Warning, police radar ahead
Smoke report	Location of police
Smokey	Police

Term	*Meaning*
Smokey dozing	Police in stopped car
Smokey on rubber	Police driving in car
Smokey on the ground	Police outside of car
Smokey's got ears	Police with CB radio
Snake den	Fire station
Spreading the greens	Police giving speeding tickets
Stepped all over you	Interfered with you
Suicide jockey	Driver of truck carrying explosives
Thermos bottle	Tanker truck
Thunder chicken	Ford Thunderbird
Tijuana taxi	Police car with flashing lights
Trading stamps	Cash
Truck 'em easy	Have a safe trip
Two-wheeler	Motorcycle
Walking on you	Interfering with your signal
Wallpaper	QSL (confirmation) card
Wall-to-Wall	Receiving good signal
Wall-to-Wall bears	Many police
Water hole	Truck stop
What am I putting on you?	What is my reading on your S-meter?
Willy Weaver	Drunk driver
Window washer	Rain
Work twenty	Place of employment
X-ray machine	Police radar

The following dictionary enables you to translate plain English into trucker terms:

Plain Language	Trucker Term
Accelerate	Hammer on; knock the slack out
Accelerator pedal	Hammer
Accumulate many road miles	Get truckin'
Amarillo or Atlanta	Big A
Ambulance	Blood box; meat wagon
Answer me	Give me a shout
Answer to a call	Comeback
(An) answer to foolish remark	Hang it in your ear
Automobile	Four wheeler
Back to you	Back
Barracuda (Plymouth)	Cuda; Fish
Beer	Brown bottles; barley pop
Beer truck	Honey wagon
Behind, or in back of	Over shoulder
Beverage truck	Bottle popper
Blocked by interference	Covered up
Boston	Bean town
Bricks	Load of rocks
California	Shakyside (refers to earthquakes)
Call	Holler; shout
Calling station	Breaker
Cannot hear	Negative copy
Can you hear me?	Got a copy?
Cash	Trading stamps

Plain Language	*Trucker Term*
Cattle truck	Portable barnyard
CB Radio	Ears; box; rig
CB turned on?	Got your ears on?
Channel 1	Basement
Channels are mostly occupied	Everybody is walking the dog
Chattanooga	Choo Choo town
Check the passengers (usually referring to females)	Check the seatcovers
Cinder truck	Salt shaker
City or town policeman	Local yokel
Concealed police car	Sitting under the leaves
Contact someone via CB	Raise
Cop giving speeding ticket	Paper hanger
Country police	Country Joe
Crystal for CB set	Rock
Cup of coffee	Hot stuff
Dallas	Big D
Died	Gone permanently 10–7
Distance	DX (refers to radio range)
Distress signal	Mayday
Drive ahead of a group, slightly over the speed limit, to lure police into view	Beat the bushes
Drive carefully	Have a safe and sound one
Driver of mobile home	Shanty shaker
Driver's license	Bouncing cardboard
Drunk driver	Willy Weaver

Plain Language	*Trucker Term*
Eavesdropping on other stations	Copying the mail
Empty truck	Load of postholes
Ending transmission	Down and gone
Ending transmission, continuing to listen	Down and on the side
Engine cover	Dog house
Examine another truck while in motion	Mobile eyeball
Excessive talker	Bucket mouth
Expressway or highway	Boulevard
FCC officials searching for illegal CB operators	Fox hunt
Federal Communications Commission	Candy man
Federal officer	Fed
Female	Beaver
Female police officer	Girlie bear; lady bear
55 miles per hour	Double nickel
Fight	Knuckle buster
Final transmission	Clear; final
Fire station	Snake den
First vehicle in a line	Front door
Flashing lights on police vehicle	Bubble machine
Florida	Bikini state
Follow closely	Holding on to your mud flaps
Ford Ranchero	Cowboy Cadillac
Ford Thunderbird	Thunder chicken

Plain Language	Trucker Term
Fort Worth	Cow town
Fuel	Motion lotion
Garage	Barn
General greeting	Good buddy
Have a safe trip	Truck 'em easy
Head of a vehicle line	Front door
Hear (How do you "read" me?)	Read
Hearty agreement	Big 10–4
Heaven	Big skip land
Helicopter or other police aircraft	Bear in the sky
High reading on CB S-meter	Breaking the needle
Highway repair crewman	Flag waver
Highway repair truck	Flag waver taxi
Home location (10–20)	Home twenty
Illegal amplifier	Foot warmer
Illegal amplifier to boost power	Linear amplifier; high gear
Indianapolis	Circle city
Inside, or passing, lane	Monster lane
Interfered with you	Stepped all over you
Interference	Background
Interference from another channel	Bleeding
Interfering with your signal	Walking on you
Interstate highway	Four lane parking lot
Invitation to speak	Go breaker; come here; come on

Fig. 10–2.   Tune in to hear road conditions. (Courtesy of E. F. Johnson Co.)

Plain Language	Trucker Term
Last truck in a line moving as a group	Back door
Last truck protecting a line warns against police overtaking the line	Back door closed
Left, or passing, lane	$50 lane; green stamp lane; side-door
Lie down and go to sleep	Get horizontal
Listening	On the by; on the side
Local cop	Little bear
Location	Fix
Location of police	Smoke report
Love and kisses	Eighty-eights (88s)
Love and kisses, best wishes	Eights and other good numbers
Lumber	Load of sticks
Many police	Open season; wall-to-wall bears; nightcrawlers
Maximum speed	Got his shoes on
Meet in person	Eyeball
Memphis	Big M
Message received	Roger
Middle truck of three-vehicle line	Sitting in the saddle
Milepost on highway	Mile marker
Milwaukee	Beer city
Money, usually for speeding ticket	Green stamps
Motorcycle	Two-wheeler

Plain Language	Trucker Term
Motorcycle cop	Evel Knievel Smokey
Moving at 55 mph	Doing the five-five
Mustang (Ford)	Horse
Next trip through	Bounce around
Nickname	Handle
No	Negatory; negative
No police	Clean
No police or hazards ahead	Good shot
Official from U.S. Department of Transportation	DOT man
OK, received	Four Roger
Operating from a base or fixed station	Anchored modulator
Operating without an illegal amplifier	Barefoot
Operator not listening to CB	Peanut butter in the ears
Overpass or bridge with little clearance	Haircut palace
Overweight truck	Fat load
Passed me rapidly	Blew my doors off
Passing lane	Bullet lane
Pay speeding ticket	Feed the bears
Pickup truck	Pickum-up
Pigs	Four-legged go-go dancers
Pigs for market	Go-Go girls
Place of employment	Work twenty
Place to sleep	Nap trap
Police	Big brother; black and whites; Smokey

Plain Language	Trucker Term
Police aircraft	Bear in the air; Eye in the sky
Police are in pursuit	Foot in the carburetor
Police car with flashing lights	Advertising; Tijuana taxi
Police changing direction	Flip-flopping bears
Police checking speed with radar	Picture taking
Police driving in car	Smokey on rubber
Police in stopped car	Smokey dozing
Police giving speeding tickets	Spreading the greens
Police on median strip	Hiding in the grass
Police officer	Smokey bear
Police outside of car	Smokey on the ground
Police radar	Camera; picture-taker; x-ray machine
Police station	Bear cage; bear cave
Police stopping vehicles driving over speed limit	Bagging
Police with CB radio	Smokey's got ears
Police with radar	Kodiak with a kodak
Porno publications	Funny books
Press accelerator to the floor	Drop the hammer down
Pressing accelerator	Got my foot in it
Prison	Slammer
Prostitute	Dress for sale
Putting out a good signal	Getting out
Pursuit car of police radar team	Catch car; chase car

Plain Language	*Trucker Term*
QSL (confirmation) card	Wallpaper
Radar	Electric teeth
Radar set	Camera; kodak; picture box
Rain	Window washer
Receive a speeding ticket	Feed the bears
Receiving good signal	Wall-to-wall
Refrigerated truck	Reefer
Repeat your last message	Come again
Request to communicate on channel	Break; breaker; break break
Restaurant	Bean store
Rest room	Coke stop
Return trip	Backslide; backstroke; flip-flop; flipper
Road with toll booth	Green stamp road
Running off the side of highway	Dropping it off the shoulder
San Francisco	Bay city
School bus	Blinkin' winkin'; kiddie car
73s and 88s, which mean "best regards" and "love and kisses"	Good numbers
Short contact	One time
Sheriff's deputy	County mountie
Shut down the CB set	Cut the coax
Sign-off (*see* 73 and 88)	Pass the numbers
Sleep	Cut some Zs

Plain Language	Trucker Term
Slipper road	Skating rink
Slow down	Back down; back off the hammer; flaps down; hammer off; hammer up
Slow-moving vehicle	Dead pedal
Snow	Fluff stuff
Snyder truck	Big orange
Social CB gathering	Jamboree
Soon	Short short
Speak to	Catch
Speed limit	On the peg
Speeding ticket	Bear bite
Speeding ticket received	Bit on the britches
(Speech pause, for example, "um")	Mercy
Speed up	Hammer down
Speeding up	Shoveling coal
State police	Boogie man
Steal a call sign	Bootleg
Stop transmitting	Back out
Strong signal	Bodacious
Strong signal being received	Bending my windows
Switch that turns off CB set	Big switch
Switch to another channel	Make a trip
Talk	Modulate; jaw jacking
Tampa	Cigar city
Tanker truck	Thermos bottle
Telephone	Land line
Thunderbird (Ford)	Bird

Plain Language	*Trucker Term*
Ticket for speeding	Christmas card; coupon
Tire problem	Bubble trouble
Tired	Checking my eyelids for pin holes
Toll booth	Piggy bank
Town police	City kitty
Tractor-trailer	Bucket of bolts; country Cadillac; eighteen wheeler; set of doubles
Truck driver	Road jockey
Truck fuel	Go juice
Truck stop	Water hole
Tunnel	Hole in the wall
Turn around	Flop it
Turn left	Hang a left
Turn off the CB set	Cut loose
Turn right	Hang a right
Tucson	Big T
TV	Boob toob
Understand	Dig you out
Unmarked police car	Brown paper bag; plain brown (or other color) wrapper
Unoccupied police car	Dummy
U-turn	Bang a U-ee
Vehicle for transporting animals	Bull rack

Plain Language	Trucker Term
Vehicle not equipped with CB rig	Bear bait; bear food; bear meat
Vehicle stopped for speeding	Pigeon
Voice becoming lost in noise	Breaking up
Warning, police radar ahead	Smile and comb your hair; brush your teeth and comb your hair
Weigh station	Chicken coop
Weigh station inspector	Chicken inspector
Weigh station is closed	Chicken coop is clean
What is my reading on your S-meter?	What am I putting on you?
Woman passenger	Seat cover
Wrecker	Draggin' wagon
Yes	Charlie

11

CB Rules and Regulations*

Part 95 / Citizens Radio Service

FEDERAL COMMUNICATIONS COMMISSION

* Author's note: This chapter contains the Citizens Radio Service rules and regulations as published by the FCC effective April 1975. The Appendix amendments effective March 1976 have been incorporated herein.

Contents—Part 95*

Subpart A—General

Sec.
95.1   Basis and purpose.
95.3   Definitions.
95.5   Policy governing the assignment of frequencies.
95.6   Types of operation authorized.
95.7   General citizenship requirements.

Subpart B—Applications and Licenses

95.11   Station authorization required.
95.13   Eligibility for station license.
95.14   Mailing address furnished by licensee.
95.15   Filing of applications.
95.17   Who may sign applications.
95.19   Standard forms to be used.
95.25   Amendment or dismissal of application.
95.27   Transfer of license prohibited.
95.29   Defective applications.
95.31   Partial grant.
95.33   License term.
95.35   Changes in transmitters and authorized stations.
95.37   Limitations on antenna structures.

Subpart C—Technical Regulations

95.41   Frequencies available.
95.43   Transmitter power.
95.44   External radio frequency power amplifiers pro-
        hibited.
95.45   Frequency tolerance.

* Sections of these rules and regulations have been left open
  by the FCC to accommodate future amendments.

Sec.
95.47   Types of emission.
95.49   Emission limitations.
95.51   Modulation requirements.
95.53   Compliance with technical requirements.
95.55   Acceptability of transmitters for licensing.
95.57   Procedure for type acceptance of equipment.
95.58   Additional requirements for type acceptance.
95.59   Submission of noncrystal controlled Class C station transmitters for type approval.
95.61   Type approval of receiver-transmitter combinations.
95.63   Minimum equipment specifications.
95.65   Test procedure.
95.67   Certificate of type approval.

Subpart D—Station Operating Requirements

Sec.
95.83   Prohibited uses.
95.85   Emergency and assistance to motorist use.
95.87   Operation by, or on behalf of, persons other than the licensee.
95.89   Telephone answering services.
95.91   Duration of transmissions.
95.93   Tests and adjustments.
95.95   Station identification.
95.97   Operator license requirements.
95.101 Posting station license and transmitter identification cards or plates.
95.103 Inspection of stations and station records.
95.105 Current copy of rules required.
95.107 Inspection and maintenance of tower marking and lighting, and associated control equipment.
95.111 Recording of tower light inspections.
95.113 Answers to notices of violations.
95.115 False signals.
95.117 Station location.
95.119 Control points, dispatch points, and remote control.
95.121 Civil defense communications.

Subpart E—Operation of Citizens Radio Stations in the United States by Canadians

Sec.
95.131   Basis, purpose and scope.
95.133   Permit required.
95.135   Application for permit.
95.137   Issuance of permit.
95.139   Modification or cancellation of permit.
95.141   Possession of permit.
95.143   Knowledge of rules required.
95.145   Operating conditions.
95.147   Station identification.

AUTHORITY: §§ 95.1 to 95.147 issued under secs. 4, 303, 48 Stat. 1066, 1082, as amended; 47 U.S.C. 154, 303. Interpret or apply 48 Stat. 1064–1068, 1081–1105, as amended; 47 U.S.C. Sub-chap. I, III–VI.

SUBPART A—GENERAL

§ 95.1 Basis and purpose.

The rules and regulations set forth in this part are issued pursuant to the provisions of Title III of the Communications Act of 1934, as amended, which vests authority in the Federal Communications Commission to regulate radio transmissions and to issue licenses for radio stations. These rules are designed to provide for private short-distance radiocommunications service for the business or personal activities of licensees, for radio signaling, for the control of remote objects or devices by means of radio; all to the extent that these uses are not specifically prohibited in this part. They also provide for procedures whereby manufacturers of radio equipment to be used or operated in the Citizens Radio Service may obtain type acceptance and/or type approval of such equipment as may be appropriate.

§ 95.3 Definitions.

For the purpose of this part, the following definitions shall be applicable. For other definitions, refer to Part 2 of this chapter.

a. Definitions of services.

Citizens Radio Service. A radiocommunications service of fixed, land, and mobile stations intended for short-distance personal or business radiocommunications, radio signaling, and control of remote objects or devices by radio; all to the extent that these uses are not specifically prohibited in this part.

Fixed service. A service of radiocommunication between specified fixed points.

Mobile service. A service of radiocommunication between mobile and land stations or between mobile stations.

b. Definitions of stations.

Base station. A land station in the land mobile service carrying on a service with land mobile stations.

Class A station. A station in the Citizens Radio Service licensed to be operated on an assigned frequency in the 460–470 MHz band with a transmitter output power of not more than 50 watts.

Class B station. (All operations terminated as of November 1, 1971.)

Class C station. A station in the Citizens Radio Service licensed to be operated on an authorized frequency in the 26.96–27.23 MHz band, or on the frequency 27.255 MHz, for the control of remote objects or devices by radio, or for the remote actuation of devices which are used solely as a means of attracting attention, or on an authorized frequency in the 72–76 MHz band for the radio control of models used for hobby purposes only.

Class D station. A station in the Citizens Radio Service licensed to be operated for radiotelephony, only, on an authorized frequency in the 26.96–27.23 MHz band and on the frequency 27.255 MHz.

Fixed station. A station in the fixed service.

Land station. A station in the mobile service not intended for operation while in motion. (Of the various types of land stations, only the base station is pertinent to this part.)

Mobile station. A station in the mobile service intended to be used while in motion or during halts at unspecified points. (For the purposes of this part, the term includes hand-carried and pack-carried units.)

c. Miscellaneous definitions.

Antenna structures. The term "antenna structures" includes the radiating system, its supporting structures and any appurtenances mounted thereon.

Assigned frequency. The frequency appearing on a station authorization from which the carrier frequency may deviate by an amount not to exceed that permitted by the frequency tolerance.

Authorized bandwidth. The maximum permissible bandwidth for the particular emission used. This shall be the occupied bandwidth or necessary bandwidth, whichever is greater.

Carrier power. The average power at the output terminals of a transmitter (other than a transmitter having a suppressed, reduced or controlled carrier) during one radio frequency cycle under conditions of no modulation.

Control point. A control point is an operating position which is under the control and supervision of the licensee, at which a person immediately responsible for the proper operation of the transmitter is stationed, and at which adequate means are available to aurally monitor all transmissions and to render the transmitter inoperative.

Dispatch point. A dispatch point is any position from which messages may be transmitted under the supervision of the person at a control point.

Double sideband emission. An emission in which both upper and lower sidebands resulting from the modulation of a particular carrier are transmitted. The carrier, or a portion thereof, also may be present in the emission.

External radio frequency power amplifiers. As defined in § 2.815(a) and as used in this part, an external radio frequency power amplifier is any device which, (1) when used in conjunction with a radio transmitter as a signal source is capable of amplification of that signal, and (2) is not an integral part of a radio transmitter as manufactured.

Harmful interference. Any emission, radiation or induction which endangers the functioning of a radio-navigation service or other safety service or seriously degrades, obstructs or repeatedly interrupts a radio-communication service operating in accordance with applicable laws, treaties, and regulations.

Man-made structure. Any construction other than a tower, mast or pole.

Mean power. The power at the output terminals of a transmitter during normal operation, averaged over a time sufficiently long compared with the period of the lowest frequency encountered in the modulation. A time of $\frac{1}{10}$ second during which the mean power is greatest will be selected normally.

Necessary bandwidth. For a given class of emission, the minimum value of the occupied bandwidth sufficient to ensure the transmission of information at the rate and with the quality required for the system employed, under specified conditions. Emissions useful for the good functioning of the receiving equipment, as for example, the emission corresponding to the carrier of reduced carrier systems, shall be included in the necessary bandwidth.

Occupied bandwidth. The frequency bandwidth such that, below its lower and above its upper frequency limits, the mean powers radiated are each equal to 0.5% of the total mean power radiated by a given emission.

Omnidirectional antenna. An antenna designed so the maximum radiation in any horizontal direction is within 3 dB of the minimum radiation in any horizontal direction.

Peak envelope power. The average power at the output terminals of a transmitter during one radio frequency cycle at the highest crest of the modulation envelope, taken under conditions of normal operation.

Person. The term "person" includes an individual, partnership, association, joint-stock company, trust or corporation.

Remote control. The "remote control" when applied to the use or operation of a citizens radio station means control of the transmitting equipment of that station from any place other than the location of the transmitting equipment, except that direct mechanical control or direct electrical control by wired connections of transmitting equipment from some other point on the same premises, craft or vehicle shall not be considered to be remote control.

Single sideband emission. An emission in which only one sideband is transmitted. The carrier, or a portion thereof, also may be present in the emission.

Station authorization. Any construction permit, license, or special temporary authorization issued by the Commission.

§ 95.5 **Policy governing the assignment of frequencies.**

a. The frequencies which may be assigned to Class A stations in the Citizens Radio Service, and the frequencies which are available for use by Class C or Class D stations are listed in Subpart C of this part. Each frequency available for assignment to, or use by, stations in this service is available on a shared basis only, and will not be assigned for the exclusive use of any one applicant; however, the use of a particular frequency may be restricted to (or in) one or more specified geographical areas.

b. In no case will more than one frequency be assigned to Class A stations for the use of a single applicant in any given area until it has been demonstrated conclusively to the Commission that the assignment of an additional frequency is essential to the operation proposed.

c. All applicants and licensees in this service shall cooperate in the selection and use of the frequencies assigned or authorized, in order to minimize interference and thereby obtain the most effective use of the authorized facilities.

d. Simultaneous operation on more than one frequency in the 72–76 MHz band by a transmitter or transmitters of a single licensee is prohibited whenever such operation will cause harmful interference to the operation of other licensees in this service.

§ 95.6   Types of operation authorized.

a. Class A stations may be authorized as mobile stations, as base stations, as fixed stations, or as base or fixed stations to be operated at unspecified or temporary locations.

b. Class C and Class D stations are authorized as mobile stations only; however, they may be operated at fixed locations in accordance with other provisions of this part.

§ 95.7   General citizenship requirements.

A station license shall not be granted to or held by a foreign government or a representative thereof.

[§ *95.7 revised eff. 2–5–75; VI (75)–1*]

SUBPART B—APPLICATIONS AND LICENSES

§ 95.11   Station authorization required.

No radio station shall be operated in the Citizens Radio Service except under and in accordance with an authorization granted by the Federal Communications Commission.

§ 95.13   Eligibility for station license.

a. Subject to the general restrictions of § 95.7, any person is eligible to hold an authorization to operate a station in the Citizens Radio Service: *Provided,* That if an applicant for a Class A or Class D station authorization is an individual or partnership, such individual or each partner is eighteen or more years of age; or if an applicant for a Class C station authorization is an individual or partnership, such individual or each partner is twelve or more years of age. An unincorporated association, when licensed under the provisions of this paragraph, may upon specific prior approval of the Commission provide radiocommunications for its members.

NOTE: While the basis of eligibility in this service includes any state, territorial, or local governmental entity, or any agency operating by the authority of such governmental entity, including any duly authorized state, territorial, or local civil defense agency, it should be noted that the frequencies available to stations in this service are shared without distinction between all licensees and that no protection is afforded to the communications of any station in this service from interference which may be caused by the authorized operation of other licensed stations.

b. [Reserved]
c. No person shall hold more than one Class C and one Class D station license.

§ 95.14   Mailing address furnished by licensee.

Each application shall set forth and each licensee shall furnish the Commission with an address in the United States to be used by the Commission in serving documents or directing correspondence to that licensee. Unless any licensee advises the Commission to the contrary, the address contained in the licensee's most recent application will be used by the Commission for this purpose.

[§ *95.14 added new eff. 2–5–75; VI(75)–1*]

§ 95.15 Filing of applications.

a. To assure that necessary information is supplied in a consistent manner by all persons, standard forms are prescribed for use in connection with the majority of applications and reports submitted for Commission consideration. Standard numbered forms applicable to the Citizens Radio Service are discussed in § 95.19 and may be obtained from the Washington, D.C., 20554, office of the Commission, or from any of its engineering field offices.

b. All formal applications for Class C or Class D new, modified, or renewal station authorizations shall be submitted to the Commission's office at 334 York Street, Gettysburg, Pa. 17325. Applications for Class A station authorizations, applications for consent to transfer of control of a corporation holding any citizens radio station authorization, requests for special temporary authority or other special requests, and correspondence relating to an application for any class citizens radio station authorization shall be submitted to the Commission's Office at Washington, D.C. 20554, and should be directed to the attention of the Secretary. Beginning January 1, 1973, applicants for Class A stations in the Chicago Regional Area, defined in § 95.19, shall submit their applications to the Commission's Chicago Regional Office. The address of the Regional Office will be announced at a later date. Applications involving Class A or Class D station equipment which is neither type approved nor crystal controlled, whether of commercial or home construction, shall be accompanied by supplemental data describing in detail the design and construction of the transmitter and methods employed in testing it to determine compliance with the technical requirements set forth in Subpart C of this part.

c. Unless otherwise specified, an application shall be filed at least 60 days prior to the date on which it is desired that Commission action thereon be completed. In any case where the applicant has made timely and sufficient application for renewal of license, in accordance with the Commission's rules, no license with reference to any activity of a continuing nature shall expire until such application shall have been finally determined.

d. Failure on the part of the applicant to provide all the information required by the application form, or to supply the necessary exhibits or supplementary statements may constitute a defect in the application.

e. Applicants proposing to construct a radio station on a site located on land under the jurisdiction of the U.S. Forest Service, U.S. Department of Agriculture, or the Bureau of Land Management, U.S. Department of the Interior, must supply the information and must follow the procedure prescribed by § 1.70 of this chapter.

§ 95.17   Who may sign applications.

a. Except as provided in paragraph (b) of this section, applications, amendments thereto, and related statements of fact required by the Commission shall be personally signed by the applicant, if the applicant is an individual; by one of the partners, if the applicant is a partnership; by an officer, if the applicant is a corporation; or by a member who is an officer, if the applicant is an unincorporated association. Applications, amendments, and related statements of fact filed on behalf of eligible government entities, such as states and territories of the United States and political subdivisions thereof, the District of Columbia, and units of local government, including incorporated municipalities, shall be signed by such duly elected or appointed officials as may be competent to do so under the laws of the applicable jurisdiction.

b. Applications, amendments thereto, and related statements of fact required by the Commission may be signed by the applicant's attorney in case of the applicant's physical disability or of his absence from the United States. The attorney shall in that event separately set forth the reason why the application is not signed by the applicant. In addition, if any matter is stated on the basis of the attorney's belief only (rather than his knowledge), he shall separately set forth his reasons for believing that such statements are true.

c. Only the original of applications, amendments, or related statements of fact need be signed; copies may be conformed.

d. Applications, amendments, and related statements of fact need not be signed under oath. Willful false statements made therein, however, are punishable by fine and imprisonment. U.S. Code, Title 18, section 1001, and by appropriate administrative sanctions, including revocation of station license pursuant to section 312(a) (1) of the Communications Act of 1934, as amended.

§ 95.19   Standard forms to be used.

a. *FCC Form 505, Application for Class C or D Station License in the Citizens Radio Service.* This form shall be used when:

1. Application is made for a new Class C or Class D authorization. A separate application shall be submitted for each proposed class of station.

2. Application is made for modification of any existing Class C or Class D station authorization in those cases where prior Commission approval of certain changes is required (see § 95.35).

3. Application is made for renewal of an existing Class C or Class D station authorization, or for reinstatement of such an expired authorization.

b. *FCC Form 400, Application for Radio Station Authorization in the Safety and Special Radio Services.* Except as provided in paragraph (d) of this section, this form shall be used when:

1. Application is made for a new Class A base station or fixed station authorization. Separate applications shall be submitted for each proposed base or fixed station at different fixed locations; however, all equipment intended to be operated at a single fixed location is considered to be one station which may, if necessary, be classed as both a base station and a fixed station.

2. Application is made for a new Class A station authorization for any required number of mobile units (including hand-carried and pack-carried units) to be

operated as a group in a single radiocommunication
system in a particular area. An application for Class
A mobile station authorization may be combined with
the application for a single Class A base station authorization when such mobile units are to be operated with
that base station only.

3. Application is made for station license of any Class
A base station or fixed station upon completion of construction or installation in accordance with the terms
and conditions set forth in any construction permit required to be issued for that station, or application for
extension of time within which to construct such a
station.

4. Application is made for modification of any existing Class A station authorization in those cases where
prior Commission approval of certain changes is required (see § 95.35).

5. Application is made for renewal of an existing
Class A station authorization, or for reinstatement of
such an expired authorization.

6. Each applicant in the Safety and Special Radio
Services (1) for modification of a station license involving a site change or a substantial increase in tower
height or (2) for a license for a new station must, before commencing construction, supply the environmental
information, where required, and must follow the procedure prescribed by Subpart I of Part 1 of this chapter
(§§ 1.1301 through 1.1319) unless Commission action
authorizing such construction would be a minor action
with the meaning of Subpart I of Part 1.

7. Application is made for an authorization for a
new Class A base or fixed station to be operated at unspecified or temporary locations. When one or more
individual transmitters are each intended to be operated
as a base station or as a fixed station at unspecified or
temporary locations for indeterminate periods, such
transmitters may be considered to comprise a single
station intended to be operated at temporary locations.
The application shall specify the general geographic
area within which the operation will be confined. Sufficient data must be submitted to show the need for the
proposed area of operation.

c. *FCC Form 703, Application for Consent to Transfer of Control of Corporation Holding Construction Permit or Station License.* This form shall be used when application is made for consent to transfer control of a corporation holding any citizens radio station authorization.

d. Beginning April 1, 1972, FCC Form 425 shall be used in lieu of FCC Form 400, applicants for Class A stations located in the Chicago Regional Area defined to consist of the counties listed below:

ILLINOIS

1. Boone.	19. Iroquois.	37. Moultrie.
2. Bureau.	20. Jo Daviess.	38. Ogle.
3. Carroll.	21. Kane.	39. Peoria.
4. Champaign.	22. Kankakee.	40. Piatt.
5. Christian.	23. Kendall.	41. Putnam.
6. Clark.	24. Knox.	42. Rock Island.
7. Coles.	25. Lake.	43. Sangamon.
8. Cook.	26. La Salle.	44. Shelby.
9. Cumberland.	27. Lee.	45. Stark
10. De Kalb.	28. Livingston.	46. Stephenson.
11. De Witt.	29. Logan.	47. Tazewell.
12. Douglas.	30. Macon.	48. Vermilion.
13. Du Page.	31. Marshall.	49. Warren.
14. Edgar.	32. Mason.	50. Whiteside.
15. Ford.	33. McHenry.	51. Will.
16. Fulton.	34. McLean.	52. Winnebago.
17. Grundy.	35. Menard.	53. Woodford.
18. Henry.	36. Mercer.	

INDIANA

1. Adams.	13. Fountain.	25. Lake.
2. Allen.	14. Fulton.	26. Lagrange.
3. Benton.	15. Grant.	27. La Porte.
4. Blackford.	16. Hamilton.	28. Madison.
5. Boone.	17. Hancock.	29. Marion.
6. Carroll.	18. Hendricks.	30. Marshall.
7. Cass.	19. Henry.	31. Miami.
8. Clay.	20. Howard.	32. Montgomery.
9. Clinton.	21. Huntington.	33. Morgan.
10. De Kalb.	22. Jasper.	34. Newton.
11. Delaware.	23. Jay.	35. Noble.
12. Elkhart.	24. Kosciusko.	36. Owen.

INDIANA —Continued

37. Parke.
38. Porter.
39. Pulaski.
40. Putnam.
41. Randolph.
42. St. Joseph.

43. Starke.
44. Steuben.
45. Tippecanoe.
46. Tipton.
47. Vermilion.
48. Vigo.

49. Wabash.
50. Warren.
51. Wells.
52. White.
53. Whitley.

IOWA

1. Cedar.
2. Clinton.

3. Dubuque.
4. Jackson
5. Jones.

6. Muscatine.
7. Scott.

MICHIGAN

1. Allegan.
2. Barry.
3. Berrien.
4. Branch.
5. Calhoun.
6. Cass.
7. Clinton.
8. Eaton.

9. Hillsdale.
10. Ingham.
11. Ionia.
12. Jackson.
13. Kalamazoo.
14. Kent.
15. Lake.
16. Mason.

17. Mecosta.
18. Montcalm.
19. Muskegon.
20. Newaygo.
21. Oceana.
22. Ottawa.
23. St. Joseph.
24. Van Buren.

OHIO

1. Defiance.
2. Mercer.

3. Paulding.
4. Van Wert.

5. Williams.

WISCONSIN

1. Adams.
2. Brown.
3. Calumet.
4. Columbia.
5. Dane.
6. Dodge.
7. Door.
8. Fond du Lac.
9. Grant.
10. Green.
11. Green Lake.

12. Iowa.
13. Jefferson.
14. Juneau.
15. Kenosha.
16. Kewaunee.
17. Lafayette.
18. Manitowoc.
19. Marquette.
20. Milwaukee.
21. Outagamie.
22. Ozaukee.

23. Racine.
24. Richland.
25. Rock.
26. Sauk.
27. Sheboygan.
28. Walworth.
29. Washington.
30. Waukesha.
31. Waupaca.
32. Waushara.
33. Winnebago.

§ 95.25   Amendment or dismissal of application.

a. Any application may be amended upon request of the applicant as a matter of right prior to the time the application is granted or designated for hearing. Each amendment to an application shall be signed and submitted in the same manner and with the same number of copies as required for the original application.

b. Any application may, upon written request signed by the applicant or his attorney, be dismissed without prejudice as a matter of right prior to the time the application is granted or designated for hearing.

§ 95.27 Transfer of license prohibited.

A station authorization in the Citizens Radio Service may not be transferred or assigned. In lieu of such transfer or assignment, an application for new station authorization shall be filled in each case, and the previous authorization shall be forwarded to the Commission for cancellation.

§ 95.29 Defective applications.

a. If an applicant is requested by the Commission to file any documents or information not included in the prescribed application form, a failure to comply with such request will constitute a defect in the application.

b. When an application is considered to be incomplete or defective, such application will be returned to the applicant, unless the Commission may otherwise direct. The reason for return of the applications will be indicated, and if appropriate, necessary additions or corrections will be suggested.

§ 95.31 Partial grant.

Where the Commission, without a hearing, grants an application in part, or with any privileges, terms, or conditions other than those requested, the action of the Commission shall be considered as a grant of such application unless the applicant shall, within 30 days from the date on which such grant is made, or from its effective date if a later date is specified, file with the Commission a written rejection of the grant as made. Upon receipt of such rejection, the Commission will vacate its original action upon the application and, if appropriate, set the application for hearing.

§ 95.33   License term.

Licenses for stations in the Citizens Radio Service will normally be issued for a term of 5 years from the date of original issuance, major modification, or renewal.

§ 95.35   Changes in transmitters and authorized stations.

Authority for certain changes in transmitters and authorized stations must be obtained from the Commission before the changes are made, while other changes do not require prior Commission approval. The following paragraphs of this section describe the conditions under which prior Commission approval is or is not necessary.

a. Proposed changes which will result in operation inconsistent with any of the terms of the current authorization require that an application for modification of license be submitted to the Commission. Application for modification shall be submitted in the same manner as an application for a new station license, and the licensee shall forward his existing authorization to the Commission for cancellation immediately upon receipt of the superseding authorization. Any of the following changes to authorized stations may be made only upon approval by the Commission:

1. Increase the overall number of transmitters authorized.

2. Change the presently authorized location of a Class A fixed or base station or control point.

3. Move, change the height of, or erect a Class A station antenna structure.

4. Make any change in the type of emission or any increase in bandwidth of emission or power of a Class A station.

5. Addition or deletion of control point(s) for an authorized transmitter of a Class A station.

6. Change or increase the area of operation of a Class A mobile station or a Class A base or fixed station authorized to be operated at temporary locations.

7. Change the operating frequency of a Class A station.

b. When the name of a licensee is changed (without changes in the ownership, control, or corporate structure), or when the mailing address of the licensee is changed (without changing the authorized location of the base or fixed Class A station) a formal application for modification of the license is not required. However, the licensee shall notify the Commission promptly of these changes. The notice, which may be in letter form, shall contain the name and address of the licensee as they appear in the Commission's records, the new name and/or address, as the case may be, and the call signs and classes of all radio stations authorized to the licensee under this part. The notice concerning Class C or D radio stations shall be sent to Federal Communications Commission, Gettysburg, Pa. 17325, and a copy shall be maintained with the records of the station. The notice concerning Class A stations shall be sent to (1) Secretary, Federal Communications Commission, Washington, D.C. 20554, and (2) to Engineer in Charge of the Radio District in which the station is located, and a copy shall be maintained with the license of the station until a new license is issued.

c. Proposed changes which will not depart from any of the terms of the outstanding authorization for the station may be made without prior Commission approval. Included in such changes is the substitution of transmitting equipment at any station, provided that the equipment employed is included in the Commission's "Radio Equipment List," and is listed as acceptable for use in the appropriate class of station in this service. Provided it is crystal-controlled and otherwise complies with the power, frequency tolerance, emission and modulation percentage limitations prescribed, non-type accepted equipment may be substituted at:

1. Class C stations operated on frequencies in the 26.99–27.26 MHz band;

2. Class D stations until November 22, 1974.

d. Transmitting equipment type accepted for use in Class D stations shall not be modified by the user. Changes which are specifically prohibited include:

1. Internal or external connection or addition of any part, device or accessory not included by the manufacturer with the transmitter for its type acceptance. This shall not prohibit the external connection of

antennas or antenna transmission lines, antenna switches, passive networks for coupling transmission lines or antennas to transmitters, or replacement of microphones.

2. Modification in any way not specified by the transmitter manufacturer and not approved by the Commission.

3. Replacement of any transmitter part by a part having different electrical characteristics and ratings from that replaced unless such part is specified as a replacement by the transmitter manufacturer.

4. Substitution or addition of any transmitter oscillator crystal unless the crystal manufacturer or transmitter manufacturer has made an express determination that the crystal type, as installed in the specific transmitter type, will provide that transmitter type with the capability of operating within the frequency tolerance specified in Section 95.45(a).

5. Addition or substitution of any component, crystal or combination of crystals, or any other alteration to enable transmission on any frequency not authorized for use by the licensee.

e. Only the manufacturer of the particular unit of equipment type accepted for use in Class D stations may make the permissive changes allowed under the provisions of Part 2 of this chapter for type acceptance. However, the manufacturer shall not make any of the following changes to the transmitter without prior written authorization from the Commission:

1. Addition of any accessory or device not specified in the application for type acceptance and approved by the Commission in granting said type acceptance.

2. Addition of any switch, control, or external connection.

3. Modification to provide capability for an additional number of transmitting frequencies.

§ 95.37 Limitations on antenna structures.

a. Except as provided in paragraph (b) of this section, an antenna for a Class A station which exceeds the following height limitations may not be erected or used unless notice has been filed with both the FAA on

FAA Form 7460–1 and with the Commission on Form 714 or on the license application form, and prior approval by the Commission has been obtained for:

1. Any construction or alteration of more than 200 feet in height above ground level at its site (§ 17.7(a) of this chapter).

2. Any construction or alteration of greater height than an imaginary surface extending outward and upward at one of the following slopes (§ 17.7(b) of this chapter):

I. 100 to 1 for a horizontal distance of 20,000 feet from the nearest point of the nearest runway of each airport with at least one runway more than 3,200 feet in length, excluding heliports, and seaplane bases without specified boundaries, if that airport is either listed in the Airport Directory of the current Airman's Information Manual or is operated by a Federal military agency.

II. 50 to 1 for a horizontal distance of 10,000 feet from the nearest point of the nearest runway of each airport with its longest runway no more than 3,200 feet in length, excluding heliports, and seaplane bases without specified boundaries, if that airport is either listed in the Airport Directory or is operated by a Federal military agency.

III. 25 to 1 for a horizontal distance of 5,000 feet from the nearest point of the nearest landing and take-off area of each heliport listed in the Airport Directory or operated by a Federal military agency.

3. Any construction or alteration on any airport listed in the Airport Directory of the current Airman's Information Manual (§ 17.7(c) of this chapter).

b. A notification to the Federal Aviation Administration is not required for any of the following construction or alteration of Class A station antenna structures.

1. Any object that would be shielded by existing structures of a permanent and substantial character or by natural terrain or topographic features of equal or greater height, and would be located in the congested area of a city, town, or settlement where it is evident beyond all reasonable doubt that the structure so

shielded will not adversely affect safety in air navigation. Applicants claiming such exemption shall submit a statement with their application to the Commission explaining the basis in detail for their finding (§17.14(a) of this chapter).

2. Any antenna structure of 20 feet or less in height except one that would increase the height of another antenna structure (§ 17.14(b) of this chapter).

c. All antennas (both receiving and transmitting) and supporting structures associated or used in conjunction with a Class C or D Citizens Radio Station operated from a fixed location must comply with at least one of the following:

1. The antenna and its supporting structure does not exceed 20 feet in height above ground level; or

2. The antenna and its supporting structure does not exceed by more than 20 feet the height of any natural formation, tree or man-made structure on which it is mounted; or

NOTE: A man-made structure is any construction other than a tower, mast, or pole.

3. The antenna is mounted on the transmitting antenna structure of another authorized radio station and exceeds neither 60 feet above ground level nor the height of the antenna supporting structure of the other station; or

4. The antenna is mounted on and does not exceed the height of the antenna structure otherwise used solely for receiving purposes, which structure itself complies with subparagraph (1) or (2) of this paragraph.

5. The antenna is omnidirectional and the highest point of the antenna and its supporting structure does not exceed 60 feet above ground level and the highest point also does not exceed one foot in height above the established airport elevation for each 100 feet of horizontal distance from the nearest point of the nearest airport runway.

NOTE: A work sheet will be made available upon request to assist in determining the maximum permissible height of an antenna structure.

d. Class C stations operated on frequencies in the 72–76 MHz band shall employ a transmitting antenna which complies with all of the following:

1. The gain of the antenna shall not exceed that of a half-wave dipole;

2. The antenna shall be immediately attached to, and an integral part of, the transmitter; and

3. Only vertical polarization shall be used.

e. Further details as to whether an aeronautical study and/or obstruction marking and lighting may be required, and specifications for obstruction marking and lighting when required, may be obtained from Part 17 of this chapter, "Construction, Marking, and Lighting of Antenna Structures."

f. Subpart I of Part 1 of this chapter contains procedures implementing the National Environmental Policy Act of 1969. Applications for authorization of the construction of certain classes of communications facilities defined as "major actions" in § 1.305 thereof, are required to be accompanied by specified statements. Generally these classes are:

1. Antenna towers or supporting structures which exceed 300 feet in height and are not located in areas devoted to heavy industry or to agriculture.

2. Communications facilities to be located in the following areas:

I. Facilities which are to be located in an officially designated wilderness area or in an area whose designation as a wilderness is pending consideration;

II. Facilities which are to be located in an officially designated wildlife preserve or in an area whose designation as a wildlife preserve is pending consideration;

III. Facilities which will affect districts, sites, buildings, structures or objects, significant in American history, architecture, archaeology or culture, which are listed in the National Register of Historic Places or are eligible for listing (see 36 CFR 800.2 (d) and (f) and 800.10); and

IV. Facilities to be located in areas which are recognized either nationally or locally for their special scenic or recreational value.

3. Facilities whose construction will involve exten-

sive change in surface features (e.g. wetland fill, de-
forestation or water diversion).

NOTE: The provisions of this paragraph do not include the
mounting of FM, television or other antennas comparable
thereto in size on an existing building or antenna tower. The
use of existing routes, buildings and towers is an environ-
mentally desirable alternative to the construction of new
routes or towers and is encouraged.

If the required statements do not accompany the application, the pertinent facts may be brought to the attention of
the Commission by any interested person during the course
of the license term and considered de novo by the Commission.

SUBPART C—TECHNICAL REGULATIONS

§ 95.41   Frequencies available.

a. Frequencies available for assignment to Class A
stations:

1. The following frequencies or frequency pairs are
available primarily for assignment to base and mobile
stations. They may also be assigned to fixed stations as
follows:

ɪ. Fixed stations which are used to control base stations of a system may be assigned the frequency assigned
to the mobile units associated with the base station.
Such fixed stations shall comply with the following requirements if they are located within 75 miles of the
center of urbanized areas of 200,000 or more population.

a. If the station is used to control one or more base
stations located within 45 degrees of azimuth, a directional antenna having a front-to-back ratio of at least
15 dB shall be used at the fixed station. For other situations where such a directional antenna cannot be
used, a cardioid, bidirectional or omnidirectional antenna may be employed. Consistent with reasonable
design, the antenna used must, in each case, produce a
radiation pattern that provides only the coverage necessary to permit satisfactory control of each base station
and limit radiation in other directions to the extent
feasible.

b. The strength of the signal of a fixed station controlling a single base station may not exceed the signal strength produced at the antenna terminal of the base receiver by a unit of the associated mobile station, by more than 6 dB. When the station controls more than one base station, the 6 dB control-to-mobile signal difference need be verified at only one of the base station sites. The measurement of the signal strength of the mobile unit must be made when such unit is transmitting from the control station location or, if that is not practical, from a location within one-fourth mile of the control station site.

c. Each application for a control station to be authorized under the provisions of this paragraph shall be accompanied by a statement certifying that the output power of the proposed station transmitter will be adjusted to comply with the foregoing signal level limitation. Records of the measurements used to determine the signal ratio shall be kept with the station records and shall be made available for inspection by Commission personnel upon request.

d. Urbanized areas of 200,000 or more population are defined in the U.S. Census of Population, 1960, Vol. 1, table 23, page 50. The centers of urbanized areas are determined from the Appendix, page 226 of the U.S. Commerce publication "Air Line Distance Between Cities in the United States."

II. Fixed stations, other than those used to control base stations, which are located 75 or more miles from the center of an urbanized area of 200,000 or more population. The centers of urbanized areas of 200,000 or more population are listed on page 226 of the Appendix to the U.S. Department of Commerce publication "Air Line Distance Between Cities in the United States." When the fixed station is located 100 miles or less from the center of such an urbanized area, the power output may not exceed 15 watts. All fixed systems are limited to a maximum of two frequencies and must employ directional antennas with a front-to-back ratio of at least 15 dB. For two-frequency systems, separation between transmit-receive frequencies is 5 MHz.

Base and Mobile	*Mobile Only*
(MHz)	*(MHz)*
462.550	467.550
462.575	467.575
462.600	467.600
462.625	467.625
462.650	467.650
462.675	467.675
462.700	467.700
462.725	467.725

2. Conditions governing the operation of stations authorized prior to March 18, 1968:

I. All base and mobile stations authorized to operate on frequencies other than those listed in subparagraph (1) of this paragraph may continue to operate on those frequencies only until January 1, 1970.

II. Fixed stations located 100 or more miles from the center of any urbanized area of 200,000 or more population authorized to operate on frequencies other than those listed in subparagraph (1) of this paragraph will not have to change frequencies provided no interference is caused to the operation of stations in the land mobile service.

III. Fixed stations, other than those used to control base stations, located less than 100 miles (75 miles if the transmitter power output does not exceed 15 watts) from the center of any urbanized area of 200,000 or more population must discontinue operation by November 1, 1971. However, any operation after January 1, 1970, must be on frequencies listed in subparagraph (1) of this paragraph.

IV. Fixed stations, located less than 100 miles from the center of any urbanized area of 200,000 or more population, which are used to control base stations and are authorized to operate on frequencies other than those listed in subparagraph (1) of this paragraph may continue to operate on those frequencies only until January 1, 1970.

V. All fixed stations must comply with the applicable technical requirements of subparagraph (1) relating to antennas and radiated signal strength of this paragraph by November 1, 1971.

    vi. Notwithstanding the provisions of subdivisions (i) through (v) of this subparagraph, all stations authorized to operate on frequencies between 465.000 and 465.500 MHz and located within 75 miles of the center of the 20 largest urbanized areas of the United States, may continue to operate on these frequencies only until January 1, 1969. An extension to continue operation on such frequencies until January 1, 1970, may be granted to such station licensees on a case by case basis if the Commission finds that continued operation would not be inconsistent with planned usage of the particular frequency for police purposes. The 20 largest urbanized areas can be found in the U.S. Census of Population, 1960, vol. 1, table 23, page 50. The centers of urbanized areas are determined from the appendix, page 226, of the U.S. Commerce publication, "Air Line Distance Between Cities in the United States."

    b. [Reserved]

    c. Class C mobile stations may employ only amplitude tone modulation or on-off keying of the unmodulated carrier, on a shared basis with other stations in the Citizens Radio Service on the frequencies and under the conditions specified in the following tables:

    1. For the control of remote objects or devices by radio, or for the remote actuation of devices which are used solely as a means of attracting attention and subject to no protection from interference due to the operation of industrial, scientific, or medical devices within the 26.96–27.28 MHz band, the following frequencies are available:

(MHz)	*(MHz)*	*(MHz)*
26.995	27.095	27.195
27.045	27.145	[1]27.255

[1]The frequency 27.255 MHz also is shared with stations in other services.

    2. Subject to the conditions that interference will not be caused to the remote control of industrial equipment operating on the same or adjacent frequencies and to

the reception of television transmissions on Channels 4 or 5; and that no protection will be afforded from interference due to the operation of fixed and mobile stations in other services assigned to the same or adjacent frequencies in the band, the following frequencies are available solely for the radio remote control of models used for hobby purposes:

I. For the radio remote control of any model used for hobby purposes:

MHz	MHz	MHz
72.16	72.32	72.96

II. For the radio remote control of aircraft models only:

MHz	MHz	MHz
72.08	72.24	72.40
75.64		

d. The frequencies listed in the following tables are available for use by Class D mobile stations employing radiotelephony only, on a shared basis with other stations in the Citizens Radio Service, and subject to no protection from interference due to the operation of industrial, scientific, or medical devices within the 26.96–27.28 MHz band.

1. The following frequencies, commonly known as channels, may be used for communication between units of the same station (intrastation) or different stations (interstation):

MHz	Channel
26.965	1
26.975	2
26.985	3
27.005	4
27.015	5
27.025	6
27.035	7
27.055	8

27.075	10
27.105	12
27.115	13
27.125	14
27.135	15
27.155	16
27.165	17
27.175	18
27.185	19
27.205	20
27.215	21
27.225	22
27.255	23

2. The frequency 27.065 MHz (Channel 9) shall be used solely for:

I. Emergency communications involving the immediate safety of life of individuals or the immediate protection of property or

II. Communications necessary to render assistance to a motorist.

NOTE: A licensee, before using Channel 9, must make a determination that his communication is either or both (a) an emergency communication or (b) is necessary to render assistance to a motorist. To be an emergency communication, the message must have some direct relation to the immediate safety of life or immediate protection of property. If no immediate action is required, it is not an emergency. What may not be an emergency under one set of circumstances may be an emergency under different circumstances. There are many worthwhile public service communications that do not qualify as emergency communications. In the case of motorist assistance, the message must be necessary to assist a particular motorist and not, except in a valid emergency, motorists in general. If the communications are to be lengthy, the exchange should be shifted to another channel, if feasible, after contact is established. No nonemergency or nonmotorist assistance communications are permitted on Channel 9 even for the limited purpose of calling a licensee monitoring a channel to ask him to switch to another channel. Although Channel 9 may be used for marine emergencies, it should not be considered a substitute for the authorized marine distress system. The Coast Guard has stated it will not "participate directly in the Citizens Radio Service by fitting with and/or providing a watch on any Citizens Band Channel. (Coast Guard Commandant Instruction 2302.6.)"

The following are examples of permitted and prohibited types of communications. They are guidelines and are not intended to be all inclusive.

Permitted	Example message
Yes	"A tornado sighted six miles north of town."
No	"This is observation post number 10. No tornados sighted."
Yes	"I am out of gas on Interstate 95."
No	"I am out of gas in my driveway."
Yes	"There is a four-car collision at Exit 10 on the Beltway, send police and ambulance."
No	"Traffic is moving smoothly on the Beltway."
Yes	"Base to Unit 1, the Weather Bureau has just issued a thunderstorm warning. Bring the sailboat into port."
No	"Attention all motorists. The Weather Bureau advises that the snow tomorrow will accumulate 4 to 6 inches."
Yes	"There is a fire in the building on the corner of 6th and Main Streets."
No	"This is Halloween patrol unit number 3. Everything is quiet here."

The following priorities should be observed in the use of Channel 9.

1. Communications relating to an existing situation dangerous to life or property, i.e., fire, automobile accident.

2. Communications relating to a potentially hazardous situation, i.e., car stalled in a dangerous place, lost child, boat out of gas.

3. Road assistance to a disabled vehicle on the highway or street.

4. Road and street directions.

e. Upon specific request accompanying application for renewal of station authorization, a Class A station in this service, which was authorized to operate on a frequency in the 460–461 MHz band until March 31, 1967, may be assigned that frequency for continued use until not later than March 31, 1968, subject to all other provisions of this part.

§ 95.43   Transmitter power.

a. Transmitter power is the power at the transmitter output terminals and delivered to the antenna, antenna transmission line, or any other impedance-matched, radio frequency load.

1. For single sideband transmitters and other transmitters employing a reduced carrier, a suppressed carrier or a controlled carrier, used at Class D stations, transmitter power is the peak envelope power.

2. For all transmitters other than those covered by paragraph (a) (1) of this section, the transmitter power is the carrier power.

b. The transmitter power of a station shall not exceed the following values under any condition of modulation or other circumstances.

Class of station:	Transmitter power in watts
A	50
C—27.255 MHz	25
C—26.995–27.195 MHz	4
C—72–76 MHz	0.75
D—Carrier (where applicable)	4
D—Peak envelope power (where applicable)	12

§ 95.44   External radio frequency power amplifiers prohibited.

No external radio frequency power amplifier shall be used or attached, by connection, coupling attachment or in any other way at any Class D station.

NOTE: An external radio frequency power amplifier at a Class D station will be presumed to have been used where it is in the operator's possession or on his premises and there is extrinsic evidence of any operation of such Class D station in excess of power limitations provided under this rule part unless the operator of such equipment holds a station license in another radio service under which license the use of the said amplifier at its maximum rated output power is permitted.

§ 95.45   Frequency tolerance.

a. Except as provided in paragraphs (b) and (c) of this section, the carrier frequency of a transmitter in this service shall be maintained within the following percentage of the authorized frequency:

Class of station	Frequency tolerance	
	Fixed and base	Mobile
A	0.00025	0.0005
C		.005
D		.005

b. Transmitters used at Class C stations operating on authorized frequencies between 26.99 and 27.26 MHz with 2.5 watts or less mean output power, which are used solely for the control of remote objects or devices by radio (other than devices used solely as a means of attracting attention), are permitted a frequency tolerance of 0.01 percent.

c. Class A stations operated at a fixed location used to control base stations, through use of a mobile only frequency, may operate with a frequency tolerance of 0.0005 percent.

§ 95.47   Types of emission.

a. Except as provided in paragraph (e) of this section, Class A stations in this service will normally be authorized to transmit radiotelephony only. However, the use of tone signals or signaling devices solely to actuate receiver circuits, such as tone operated squelch or selective calling circuits, the primary function of which is to establish or establish and maintain voice communications, is permitted. The use of tone signals solely to attract attention is prohibited.

b. [Reserved]

c. Class C stations in this service are authorized to use amplitude tone modulation or on-off unmodulated carrier only, for the control of remote objects or devices by radio or for the remote actuation of devices which are used solely as a means of attracting attention. The transmission of any form of telegraphy, telephony or record communications by a Class C station is prohibited. Telemetering, except for the transmission of simple, short duration signals indicating the presence or absence of a condition or the occurrence of an event, is also prohibited.

d. Transmitters used at Class D stations in this service are authorized to use amplitude voice modulation, either single or double sideband. Tone signals or signalling devices may be used only to actuate receiver circuits, such as tone operated squelch or selective calling circuits, the primary function of which is to establish or maintain voice communications. The use of any signals solely to attract attention or for the control of remote objects or devices is prohibited.

e. Other types of emission not described in paragraph (a) of this section may be authorized for Class A citizens radio stations upon a showing of need therefor. An application requesting such authorization shall fully describe the emission desired, shall indicate the bandwidth required for satisfactory communication, and shall state the purpose for which such emission is required. For information regarding the classification of emissions and the calculation of bandwidth, reference should be made to Part 2 of this chapter.

§ 95.49   Emission limitations.

a. Each authorization issued to a Class A citizens radio station will show, as a prefix to the classification of the authorized emission, a figure specifying the maximum bandwidth to be occupied by the emission.

b. [Reserved]

c. The authorized bandwidth of the emission of any transmitter employing amplitude modulation shall be 8 kHz for double sideband, 4 kHz for single sideband and the authorized bandwidth of the emission of transmitters employing frequency or phase modulation (Class F2 or F3) shall be 20 kHz. The use of Class F2 and F3 emissions in the frequency band 26.96–27.28 MHz is not authorized.

d. The mean power of emissions shall be attenuated below the mean power of the transmitter in accordance with the following schedule:

1. When using emissions other than single sideband:

I. On any frequency removed from the center of the authorized bandwidth by more than 50 percent up to and including 100 percent of the authorized bandwidth: At least 25 decibels;

II. On any frequency removed from the center of the authorized bandwidth by more than 100 percent up to and including 250 percent of the authorized bandwidth: At least 35 decibels;

2. When using single sideband emissions:

I. On any frequency removed from the center of the authorized bandwidth by more than 50 percent up to and including 150 percent of the authorized bandwidth: At least 25 decibels:

II. On any frequency removed from the center of the authorized bandwidth by more than 150 percent up to and including 250 percent of the authorized bandwidth: At least 35 decibels;

3. On any frequency removed from the center of the authorized bandwidth by more than 250 percent of the authorized bandwidth: At least 43 plus $10 \log_{10}$ (mean power in watts) decibels.

e. When an unauthorized emission results in harmful interference, the Commission may, in its discretion, require appropriate technical changes in equipment to alleviate the interference.

§ 95.51   Modulation requirements.

a. When double sideband, amplitude modulation is used for telephony, the modulation percentage shall be sufficient to provide efficient communication and shall not exceed 100 percent.

b. Each transmitter for use in Class D stations, other than single sideband, suppressed carrier, or controlled carrier, for which type acceptance is requested after May 24, 1974, having more than 2.5 watts maximum output power shall be equipped with a device which automatically prevents modulation in excess of 100 percent on positive and negative peaks.

c. The maximum audio frequency required for satisfactory radiotelephone intelligibility for use in this service is considered to be 3000 Hz.

d. Transmitters for use at Class A stations shall be provided with a device which automatically will prevent greater than normal audio level from causing modulation in excess of that specified in this subpart; *Provided, however,* That the requirements of this paragraph shall not apply to transmitters authorized at mobile stations and having an output power of 2.5 watts or less.

e. Each transmitter of a Class A station which is equipped with a modulation limiter in accordance with the provisions of paragraph (d) of this section shall also be equipped with an audio low-pass filter. This audio low-pass filter shall be installed between the modulation limiter and the modulated stage and, at audio frequencies between 3 kHz and 20 kHz, shall have an attenuation greater than the attenuation at 1 kHz by at least:

$$60 \log_{10} (f/3) \text{ decibels}$$

where "f" is the audio frequency in kHz. At audio frequencies above 20 kHz, the attenuation shall be at least 50 decibels greater than the attenuation at 1 kHz.

f. Simultaneous amplitude modulation and frequency or phase modulation of a transmitter is not authorized.

g. The maximum frequency deviation of frequency modulated transmitters used at Class A stations shall not exceed ± 5 kHz.

§ 95.53 Compliance with technical requirements.

a. Upon receipt of notification from the Commission of a deviation from the technical requirements of the rules in this part, the radiations of the transmitter involved shall be suspended immediately, except for necessary tests and adjustments, and shall not be resumed until such deviation has been corrected.

b. When any citizens radio station licensee receives a notice of violation indicating that the station has been operated contrary to any of the provisions contained in Subpart C of this part, or where it otherwise appears that operation of a station in this service may not be in accordance with applicable technical standards, the Commission may require the licensee to conduct such tests as may be necessary to determine whether the equipment is capable of meeting these standards and to make such adjustments as may be necessary to assure compliance therewith. A licensee who is notified that he is required to conduct such tests and/or make adjustments must, within the time limit specified in the notice, report to the Commission the results thereof.

c. All tests and adjustments which may be required in accordance with paragraph (b) of this section shall be made by, or under the immediate supervision of, a person holding a first- or second-class commercial operator license, either radiotelephone or radio telegraph as may be appropriate for the type of emission employed. In each case, the report which is submitted to the Commission shall be signed by the licensed commercial operator. Such report shall describe the results of the tests and adjustments, the test equipment and procedures used, and shall state the type, class, and serial number of the operator's license. A copy of this report shall also be kept with the station records.

§ 95.55 Acceptability of transmitters for licensing.

Transmitters type approved or type accepted for use under this part are included in the Commission's Radio Equipment List. Copies of this list are available for public reference at the Commission's Washington, D.C., offices and field offices. The requirements for transmitters which may be operated under a license in this service are set forth in the following paragraphs.

a. Class A stations: All transmitters shall be type accepted.

b. Class C stations:

1. Transmitters operated in the band 72–76 MHz shall be type accepted.

2. All transmitters operated in the band 26.99–27.26 MHz shall be type approved, type accepted or crystal controlled.

c. Class D stations:

1. All transmitters first licensed, or marketed as specified in § 2.805 of this chapter, prior to November 22, 1974, shall be type accepted or crystal controlled.

2. All transmitters first licensed, or marketed as

specified in § 2.803 of this chapter, on or after November 22, 1974, shall be type accepted.

3. Effective November 23, 1978, all transmitters shall be type accepted.

4. Transmitters which are equipped to operate on any frequency not included in § 95.41(d) (1) may not be installed at, or used by, any Class D station unless there is a station license posted at the transmitter location, or a transmitter identification card (FCC Form 452-C) attached to the transmitter, which indicates that operation of the transmitter on such frequency has been authorized by the Commission.

d. With the exception of equipment type approved for use at a Class C station, all transmitting equipment authorized in this service shall be crystal controlled.

e. No controls, switches or other functions which can cause operation in violation of the technical regulations of this part shall be accessible from the operating panel or exterior to the cabinet enclosing a transmitter authorized in this service.

§ 95.57 Procedure for type acceptance of equipment.

a. Any manufacturer of a transmitter built for use in this service, except noncrystal controlled transmitters for use at Class C stations, may request type acceptance for such transmitter in accordance with the type acceptance requirements of this part, following the type acceptance procedure set forth in Part 2 of this chapter.

b. Type acceptance for an individual transmitter may also be requested by an applicant for a station authorization by following the type acceptance procedures set forth in Part 2 of this chapter. Such transmitters, if accepted, will not normally be included on the Commission's "Radio Equipment List", but will be individually enumerated on the station authorization.

c. Additional rules with respect to type acceptance are set forth in Part 2 of this chapter. These rules include information with respect to withdrawal of type acceptance, modification of type-accepted equipment, and limitations on the findings upon which type acceptance is based.

d. Transmitters equipped with a frequency or frequencies not listed in § 95.41(d) (1) will not be type accepted for use at Class D stations unless the transmitter is also type accepted for use in the service in which the frequency is authorized, if type acceptance in that service is required.

§ 95.58   Additional requirements for type acceptance.

a. All transmitters shall be crystal controlled.

b. Except for transmitters type accepted for use at Class A stations, transmitters shall not include any provisions for increasing power to levels in excess of the pertinent limits specified in Section 95.43.

c. In addition to all other applicable technical requirements set forth in this part, transmitters for which type acceptance is requested after May 24, 1974, for use at Class D stations shall comply with the following:

1. Single sideband transmitters and other transmitters employing reduced, suppressed or controlled carrier shall include a means for automatically preventing the transmitter power from exceeding either the maximum permissible peak envelope power or the rated peak envelope power of the transmitter, whichever is lower.

2. Multi-frequency transmitters shall not provide more than 23 transmitting frequencies, and the frequency selector shall be limited to a single control.

3. Other than the channel selector switch, all transmitting frequency determining circuitry, including crystals, employed in Class D station equipment shall be internal to the equipment and shall not be accessible from the exterior of the equipment cabinet or operating panel.

4. Single sideband transmitters shall be capable of transmitting on the upper sideband. Capability for transmission also on the lower sideband is permissible.

5. The total dissipation ratings, established by the manufacturer of the electron tubes or semiconductors which supply radio frequency power to the antenna terminals of the transmitter, shall not exceed 10 watts. For electron tubes, the rating shall be the Intermittent Commercial and Amateur Service (ICAS) plate dissipation value if established. For semiconductors, the rating

shall be the collector or device dissipation value, whichever is greater, which may be temperature de-rated to not more than 50°C.

d. Only the following external transmitter controls, connections or devices will normally be permitted in transmitters for which type acceptance is requested after May 24, 1974, for use at Class D stations. Approval of additional controls, connections or devices may be given after consideration of the function to be performed by such additions.

1. Primary power connection. (Circuitry or devices such as rectifiers, transformers, or inverters which provide the nominal rated transmitter primary supply voltage may be used without voiding the transmitter type acceptance.)

2. Microphone connection.

3. Radio frequency output power connection.

4. Audio frequency power amplifier output connector and selector switch.

5. On-off switch for primary power to transmitter. May be combined with receiver controls such as the receiver on-off switch and volume control.

6. Upper-lower sideband selector; for single sideband transmitters only.

7. Selector for choice of carrier level; for single sideband transmitters only. May be combined with sideband selector.

8. Transmitting frequency selector switch.

9. Transmit-receive switch.

10. Meter(s) and selector switch for monitoring transmitter performance.

11. Pilot lamp or meter to indicate the presence of radio frequency output power or that transmitter control circuits are activated to transmit.

e. An instruction book for the user shall be furnished with each transmitter sold and one copy (a draft or preliminary copy is acceptable providing a final copy is furnished when completed) shall be forwarded to the Commission with each request for type acceptance or type approval. The book shall contain all information necessary for the proper installation and operation of the transmitter including:

1. Instructions concerning all controls, adjustments and switches which may be operated or adjusted without causing violation of technical regulations of this part;

2. Warnings concerning any adjustment which, according to the rules of this part, may be made only by, or under the immediate supervision of, a person holding a commercial first or second class radio operator license;

3. Warnings concerning the replacement or substitution of crystals, tubes or other components which could cause violation of the technical regulations of this part and of the type acceptance or type approval requirements of Part 2 of this chapter.

4. Warnings concerning licensing requirements and details concerning the application procedures for licensing.

§ 95.59   Submission of noncrystal controlled Class C station transmitters for type approval.

Type approval of noncrystal controlled transmitters for use at Class C stations in this service may be requested in accordance with the procedure specified in Part 2 of this chapter.

§ 95.61   Type approval of receiver-transmitter combinations.

Type approval will not be issued for transmitting equipment for operation under this part when such equipment is enclosed in the same cabinet, is constructed on the same chassis in whole or in part, or is identified with a common type of model number with a radio receiver, unless such receiver has been certificated to the Commission as complying with the requirements of Part 15 of this chapter.

§ 95.63   Minimum equipment specifications.

Transmitters submitted for type approval in this service shall be capable of meeting the technical specifications contained in this part, and in addition, shall comply with the following:

a. Any basic instructions concerning the proper adjustment, use, or operation of the equipment that may be necessary shall be attached to the equipment in a suitable manner and in such positions as to be easily read by the operator.

b. A durable nameplate shall be mounted on each transmitter showing the name of the manufacturer, the type or model designation, and providing suitable space for permanently displaying the transmitter serial number, FCC type approval number, and the class of station for which approved.

c. The transmitter shall be designed, constructed, and adjusted by the manufacturer to operate on a frequency or frequencies available to the class of station for which type approval is sought. In designing the equipment, every reasonable precaution shall be taken to protect the user from high voltage shock and radio frequency burns. Connections to batteries (if used) shall be made in such a manner as to permit replacement by the user without causing improper operation of the transmitter. Generally accepted modern engineering principles shall be utilized in the generation of radio frequency currents so as to guard against unnecessary interference to other services. In cases of harmful interference arising from the design, construction, or operation of the equipment, the Commission may require appropriate technical changes in equipment to alleviate interference.

d. Controls which may effect changes in the carrier frequency of the transmitter shall not be accessible from the exterior of any unit unless such accessibility is specifically approved by the Commission.

§ 95.65   Test procedure.

Type approval tests to determine whether radio equipment meets the technical specifications contained in this part will be conducted under the following conditions:

a. Gradual ambient temperature variations from 0° to 125° F.

b. Relative ambient humidity from 20 to 95 percent. This test will normally consist of subjecting the equipment for at least three consecutive periods of 24 hours each, to a relative ambient humidity of 20, 60, and 95 percent, respectively, at a temperature of approximately 80° F.

c. Movement of transmitter or objects in the immediate vicinity thereof.

d. Power supply voltage variations normally to be encountered under actual operating conditions.

e. Additional tests as may be prescribed, if considered necessary or desirable.

§ 95.67   Certificate of type approval.

A certificate or notice of type approval, when issued to the manufacturer of equipment intended to be used or operated in the Citizens Radio Service, constitutes a recognition that on the basis of the test made, the particular type of equipment appears to have the capability of functioning in accordance with the technical specifications and regulations contained in this part: *Provided,* That all such additional equipment of the same type is properly constructed, maintained, and operated: *And provided further,* That no change whatsoever is made in the design or construction of such equipment except upon specific approval by the Commission.

SUBPART D—STATION OPERATING REQUIREMENTS

§ 95.81   Permissible communications.

Stations licensed in the Citizens Radio Service are authorized to transmit the following types of communications:

a. Communications to facilitate the personal or business activities of the licensee.

b. Communication relating to:

1. The immediate safety of life or the immediate protection of property in accordance with § 95.85.

2. The rendering of assistance to a motorist, mariner or other traveler.

3. Civil defense activities in accordance with § 95.121.

4. Other activities only as specifically authorized pursuant to § 95.87.

c. Communications with stations authorized in other radio services except as prohibited in § 95.83(a) (3).

§ 95.83   Prohibited communications.

a. A citizens radio station shall not be used:

1. For any purpose, or in connection with any activity, which is contrary to Federal, State, or local law.

2. For the transmission of communications containing obscene, indecent, profane words, language, or meaning.

3. To communicate with an Amateur Radio Service station, an unlicensed station, or foreign stations (other than as provided in Subpart E of this part) except for communications pursuant to §§ 95.85(b) and 95.121.

4. To convey program material for retransmission, live or delayed, on a broadcast facility.

NOTE: A Class A or Class D station may be used in connection with administrative, engineering, or maintenance activities of a broadcasting station; a Class A or Class C station may be used for control functions by radio which do not involve the transmission of program material; and a Class A or Class D station may be used in the gathering of news items or preparation of programs: Provided, that the actual or recorded transmissions of the Citizens radio station are not broadcast at any time in whole or in part.

5. To intentionally interfere with the communications of another station.

6. For the direct transmission of any material to the public through a public address system or similar means.

7. For the transmission of music, whistling, sound effects, or any material for amusement or entertainment purposes, or solely to attract attention.

8. To transmit the word "MAYDAY" or other international distress signals, except when the station is located in a ship, aircraft, or other vehicle which is threatened by grave and imminent danger and requests immediate assistance.

9. For advertising or soliciting the sale of any goods or services.

10. For transmitting messages in other than plain language. Abbreviations including nationally or internationally recognized operating signals, may be used only if a list of all such abbreviations and their meaning is kept in the station records and made available to any Commission representative on demand.

11. To carry on communications for hire, whether the remuneration or benefit received is direct or indirect.

§ 95.85 Emergency and assistance to motorist use.

a. All Citizens radio stations shall give priority to the emergency communications of other stations which involve the immediate safety of life of individuals or the immediate protection of property.

b. Any station in this service may be utilized during an emergency involving the immediate safety of life of individuals or the immediate protection of property for the transmission of emergency communications. It may also be used to transmit communications necessary to render assistance to a motorist.

1. When used for transmission of emergency communications certain provisions in this part concerning use of frequencies (§ 95.41(d)); prohibited uses (§ 95.83 (a) (3)); operation by or on behalf of persons other than the licensee (§ 95.87); and duration of transmissions (§ 95.91(a) and (b)) shall not apply.

2. When used for transmission of communications necessary to render assistance to a traveler, the provisions of this Part concerning duration of transmission (§ 95.91(b)) shall not apply.

3. The exemptions granted from certain rule provisions in subparagraphs (1) and (2) of this paragraph may be rescinded by the Commission at its discretion.

c. If the emergency use under paragraph (b) of this section extends over a period of 12 hours or more, notice shall be sent to the Commission in Washington, D.C., as soon as it is evident that the emergency has or will exceed 12 hours. The notice should include the identity of the stations participating, the nature of the emergency, and the use made of the stations. A single notice covering all participating stations may be submitted.

§ 95.87 Operation by, or on behalf of, persons other than the licensee.

a. Transmitters authorized in this service must be under the control of the licensee at all times. A licensee shall not transfer, assign, or dispose of, in any manner, directly or indirectly, the operating authority under his station license, and shall be responsible for the proper operation of all units of the station.

b. Citizens radio stations may be operated only by the following persons, except as provided in paragraph (c) of this section:

1. The licensee;

2. Members of the licensee's immediate family living in the same household;

3. The partners, if the licensee is a partnership, provided the communications relate to the business of the partnership;

4. The members, if the licensee is an unincorporated association, provided the communications relate to the business of the association;

5. Employees of the licensee only while acting within the scope of their employment;

6. Any person under the control or supervision of the licensee when the station is used solely for the control of remote objects or devices, other than devices used only as a means of attracting attention; and

7. Other persons, upon specific prior approval of the Commission shown on or attached to the station license, under the following circumstances:

I. Licensee is a corporation and proposes to provide private radiocommunication facilities for the transmission of messages or signals by or on behalf of its parent corporation, another subsidiary of the parent corporation, or its own subsidiary. Any remuneration or compensation received by the licensee for the use of the radiocommunication facilities shall be governed by a contract entered into by the parties concerned and the total of the compensation shall not exceed the cost of providing the facilities. Records which show the cost of service and its nonprofit or cost-sharing basis shall be maintained by the licensee.

II. Licensee proposes the shared or cooperative use of a Class A station with one or more other licensees in this service for the purpose of communicating on a regular basis with units of their respective Class A stations, or with units of other Class A stations if the communications transmitted are otherwise permissible.

The use of these private radiocommunication facilities shall be conducted pursuant to a written contract which shall provide that contributions to capital and operating expense shall be made on a nonprofit, cost-sharing basis, the cost to be divided on an equitable basis among all parties to the agreement. Records which show the cost of service and its nonprofit, cost-sharing basis shall be maintained by the licensee. In any case, however, licensee must show a separate and independent need for the particular units proposed to be shared to fulfill his own communications requirements.

III. Other cases where there is a need for other persons to operate a unit of licensee's radio station. Requests for authority may be made either at the time of the filing of the application for station license or thereafter by letter. In either case, the licensee must show the nature of the proposed use and that it relates to an activity of the licensee, how he proposes to maintain control over the transmitters at all times, and why it is not appropriate for such other person to obtain a station license in his own name. The authority, if granted, may be specific with respect to the names of the persons who re permitted to operate, or may authorize operation by unnamed persons for specific purposes. This authority may be revoked by the Commission, in its discretion, at any time.

c. An individual who was formerly a citizens radio station licensee shall not be permitted to operate any citizens radio station of the same class licensed to another person until such time as he again has been issued a valid radio station license of that class, when his license has been:

1. Revoked by the Commission.

2. Surrendered for cancellation after the institution of revocation proceedings by the Commission.

3. Surrendered for cancellation after a notice of apparent liability to forfeiture has been served by the Commission.

§ 95.89   Telephone answering services.

a. Notwithstanding the provisions of § 95.87, a licensee may install a transmitting unit of his station on the premises of a telephone answering service. The same unit may not be operated under the authorization of more than one licensee. In all cases, the licensee must enter into a written agreement with the answering service. This agreement must be kept with the licensee's station records and must provide, as a minimum, that:

1. The licensee will have control over the operation of the radio unit at all times;

2. The licensee will have full and unrestricted access to the transmitter to enable him to carry out his responsibilities under his license;

3. Both parties understand that the licensee is fully responsible for the proper operation of the citizens radio station; and

4. The unit so furnished shall be used only for the transmission of communications to other units belonging to the licensee's station.

b. A citizens radio station licensed to a telephone answering service shall not be used to relay messages or transmit signals to its customers.

§ 95.91 Duration of transmissions.

a. All communications or signals, regardless of their nature, shall be restricted to the minimum practicable transmission time. The radiation of energy shall be limited to transmissions modulated or keyed for actual permissible communications, tests, or control signals. Continuous or uninterrupted transmissions from a single station or between a number of communicating stations is prohibited, except for communications involving the immediate safety of life or property.

b. All communications between Class D stations (interstation) shall be restricted to not longer than five (5) continuous minutes. At the conclusion of this 5 minute period, or the exchange of less than 5 minutes, the participating stations shall remain silent for at least one minute.

c. All communication between units of the same Class D station (intrastation) shall be restricted to the minimum practicable transmission time.

d. The transmission of audible tone signals or a sequence of tone signals for the operation of the tone operated squelch or selective calling circuits in accordance with § 95.47 shall not exceed a total of 15 seconds duration. Continuous transmission of a subaudible tone for this purpose is permitted. For the purposes of this section, any tone or combination of tones having no frequency above 150 hertz shall be considered subaudible.

e. The transmission of permissible control signals shall be limited to the minimum practicable time necessary to accomplish the desired control or actuation of remote objects or devices. The continuous radiation of energy for periods exceeding 3 minutes duration for the purpose of transmission of control signals shall be limited to control functions requiring at least one or more changes during each minute of such transmission. However, while it is actually being used to control model aircraft in flight by means of interrupted tone modulation of its carrier, a citizens radio station may transmit a continuous carrier without being simultaneously modulated if the presence or absence of the carrier also performs a control function. An exception to the limitations contained in this paragraph may be authorized upon a satisfactory showing that a continuous control signal is required to perform a control function which is necessary to insure the safety of life or property.

§ 95.93   Tests and adjustments.

All tests or adjustments of citizens radio transmitting equipment involving an external connection to the radio frequency output circuit shall be made using a nonradiating dummy antenna. However, a brief test signal, either with or without modulation, as appropriate, may be transmitted when it is necessary to adjust a transmitter to an antenna for a new station installation or for an existing installation involving a change of antenna or change of transmitters, or when necessary for the detection, measurement, and suppression of harmonic or other spurious radiation. Test transmissions using a radiating antenna shall not exceed a total of 1 minute during any 5-minute period, shall not interfere with communications already in progress on the operating frequency, and shall be properly identified as required by § 95.95, but may otherwise be unmodulated as appropriate.

§ 95.95   Station identification.

a. The call sign of a citizens radio station shall consist of three letters followed by four digits.

b. Each transmission of the station call sign shall be made in the English language by each unit, shall be complete, and each letter and digit shall be separately and distinctly transmitted. Only standard phonetic alphabets, nationally or internationally recognized, may be used in lieu of pronunciation of letters for voice transmission of call signs. A unit designator or special identification may be used in addition to the station call sign but not as a substitute therefor.

c. Except as provided in paragraph (d) of this section, all transmissions from each unit of a citizens radio station shall be identified by the transmission of its assigned call sign at the beginning and end of each transmission or series of transmissions, but at least at intervals not to exceed ten (10) minutes.

d. Unless specifically required by the station authorization, the transmissions of a citizens radio station need not be identified when the station (1) is a Class A station which automatically retransmits the information received by radio from another station which is properly identified or (2) is not being used for telephony emission.

e. In lieu of complying with the requirements of paragraph (c) of this section, Class A base stations, fixed stations, and mobile units when communicating with base stations may identify as follows:

1. Base stations and fixed stations of a Class A radio system shall transmit their call signs at the end of each transmission or exchange of transmissions, or once each 15-minute period of a continuous exchange of communications.

2. A mobile unit of a Class A station communicating with a base station of a Class A radio system on the same frequency shall transmit once during each exchange of transmissions any unit identifier which is on file in the station records of such base station.

3. A mobile unit of Class A stations communicating with a base station of a Class A radio system on a different frequency shall transmit its call sign at the end

of each transmission or exchange of transmissions, or once each 15-minute period of a continuous exchange of communications.

§ 95.97   Operator license requirements.

a. No operator license is required for the operation of a citizens radio station except that stations manually transmitting Morse Code shall be operated by the holders of a third or higher class radiotelegraph operator license.

b. Except as provided in paragraph (c) of this section, all transmitter adjustments or tests while radiating energy during or coincident with the construction, installation, servicing, or maintenance of a radio station in this service, which may affect the proper operation of such stations, shall be made by or under the immediate supervision and responsibility of a person holding a first- or second-class commercial radio operator license, either radiotelephone or radio telegraph, as may be appropriate for the type of emission employed, and such person shall be responsible for the proper functioning of the station equipment at the conclusion of such adjustments or tests. Further, in any case where a transmitter adjustment which may affect the proper operation of the transmitter has been made while not radiating energy by a person not the holder of the required commercial radio operator license or not under the supervision of such licensed operator, other than the factory assembling or repair of equipment, the transmitter shall be checked for compliance with the technical requirements of the rules by a commercial radio operator of the proper grade before it is placed on the air.

c. Except as provided in § 95.53 and in paragraph (d) of this section, no commercial radio operator license is required to be held by the person performing transmitter adjustments or tests during or coincident with the construction, installation, servicing, or maintenance of Class C transmitters, or Class D transmitters used at stations authorized prior to May 24, 1974: *Provided,* That there is compliance with all of the following conditions:

1. The transmitting equipment shall be crystal-controlled with a crystal capable of maintaining the station frequency within the prescribed tolerance;

2. The transmitting equipment either shall have been factory assembled or shall have been provided in kit form by a manufacturer who provided all components together with full and detailed instructions for their assembly by nonfactory personnel;

3. The frequency determining elements of the transmitter, including the crystal(s) and all other components of the crystal oscillator circuit, shall have been preassembled by the manufacturer, pretuned to a specific available frequency, and sealed by the manufacturer so that replacement of any component or any adjustment which might cause off-frequency operation cannot be made without breaking such seal and thereby voiding the certification of the manufacturer required by this paragraph;

4. The transmitting equipment shall have been so designed that none of the transmitter adjustments or tests normally performed during or coincident with the installation, servicing, or maintenance of the station, or during the normal rendition of the service of the station, or during the final assembly of kits or partially preassembled units, may reasonably be expected to result in off-frequency operation, excessive input power, overmodulation, or excessive harmonics or other spurious emissions; and

5. The manufacturer of the transmitting equipment or of the kit from which the transmitting equipment is assembled shall have certified in writing to the purchaser of the equipment (and to the Commission upon request) that the equipment has been designed, manufactured, and furnished in accordance with the specifications contained in the foregoing subparagraphs of this paragraph. The manufacturer's certification concerning design and construction features of Class C or Class D station transmitting equipment, as required if the provisions of this paragraph are invoked, may be specific as to a particular unit of transmitting equipment or general as to a group or model of such equipment, and

may be in any form adequate to assure the purchaser of the equipment or the Commission that the conditions described in this paragraph have been fulfilled.

d. Any tests and adjustments necessary to correct any deviation of a transmitter of any Class of station in this service from the technical requirements of the rules in this part shall be made by, or under the immediate supervision of, a person holding a first- or second-class commercial operator license, either radiotelephone or radiotelegraph, as may be appropriate for the type of emission employed.

§ 95.101   Posting station license and transmitter identification cards or plates.

a. The current authorization, or a clearly legible photocopy thereof, for each station (including units of a Class C or Class D station) operated at a fixed location shall be posted at a conspicuous place at the principal fixed location from which such station is controlled, and a photocopy of such authorization shall also be posted at all other fixed locations from which the station is controlled. If a photocopy of the authorization is posted at the principal control point, the location of the original shall be stated on that photocopy. In addition, an executed Transmitter Identification Card (FCC Form 452–C) or a plate of metal or other durable substance, legibly indicating the call sign and the licensee's name and address, shall be affixed, readily visible for inspection, to each transmitter operated at a fixed location when such transmitter is not in view of, or is not readily accessible to, the operator of at least one of the locations at which the station authorization or a photocopy thereof is required to be posted.

b. The current authorization for each station operated as a mobile station shall be retained as a permanent part of the station records, but need not be posted. In addition, an executed Transmitter Identification Card (FCC Form 452–C) or a plate of metal or other durable substance, legibly indicating the call sign and the licensee's name and address, shall be affixed, readily visible for inspection, to each of such transmitters:

Provided, That, if the transmitter is not in view of the location from which it is controlled, or is not readily accessible for inspection, then such card or plate shall be affixed to the control equipment at the transmitter operating position or posted adjacent thereto.

§ 95.103   Inspection of stations and station records.

All stations and records of stations in the Citizens Radio Service shall be made available for inspection upon the request of an authorized representative of the Commission made to the licensee or to his representative (see § 1.6 of this chapter). Unless otherwise stated in this part, all required station records shall be maintained for a period of at least 1 year.

§ 95.105   Current copy of rules required.

Each licensee in this service shall maintain as a part of his station records a current copy of Part 95, Citizens Radio Service, of this chapter.

§ 95.107   Inspection and maintenance of tower marking and lighting, and associated control equipment.

The licensee of any radio station which has an antenna structure required to be painted and illuminated pursuant to the provisions of section 303(q) of the Communications Act of 1934, as amended, and Part 17 of this chapter, shall perform the inspection and maintain the tower marking and lighting, and associated control equipment, in accordance with the requirements set forth in Part 17 of this chapter.

§ 95.111   Recording of tower light inspections.

When a station in this service has an antenna structure which is required to be illuminated, appropriate entries shall be made in the station records in conformity with the requirements set forth in Part 17 of this chapter.

§ 95.113   Answers to notices of violations.

a. Any licensee who appears to have violated any provision of the Communications Act or any provision of this chapter shall be served with a written notice calling the facts to his attention and requesting a statement concerning the matter. FCC Form 793 may be used for this purpose.

b. Within 10 days from receipt of notice or such other period as may be specified, the licensee shall send a written answer, in duplicate, direct to the office of the Commission originating the notice. If an answer cannot be sent nor an acknowledgment made within such period by reason of illness or other unavoidable circumstances, acknowledgment and answer shall be made at the earliest practicable date with a satisfactory explanation of the delay.

c. The answer to each notice shall be complete in itself and shall not be abbreviated by reference to other communications or answers to other notices. In every instance the answer shall contain a statement of the action taken to correct the condition or omission complained of and to preclude its recurrence. If the notice relates to violations that may be due to the physical or electrical characteristics of transmitting apparatus, the licensee must comply with the provisions of § 95.53, and the answer to the notice shall state fully what steps, if any, have been taken to prevent future violations, and, if any new apparatus is to be installed, the date such apparatus was ordered, the name of the manufacturer, and the promised date of delivery. If the installation of such apparatus requires a construction permit, the file number of the application shall be given, or if a file number has not been assigned by the Commission, such identification shall be given as will permit ready identification of the application. If the notice of violation relates to lack of attention to or improper operation of the transmitter, the name and license number of the operator in charge, if any, shall also be given.

§ 95.115   False signals.

No person shall transmit false or deceptive communications by radio or identify the station he is operating by means of a call sign which has not been assigned to that station.

§ 95.117 Station location.

a. The specific location of each Class A base station and each Class A fixed station and the specific area of operation of each Class A mobile station shall be indicated in the application for license. An authorization may be granted for the operation of a Class A base station or fixed station in this service at unspecified temporary fixed locations within a specified general area of operation. However, when any unit or units of a base station or fixed station authorized to be operated at temporary locations actually remains or is intended to remain at the same location for a period of over a year, application for separate authorization specifying the fixed location shall be made as soon as possible but not later than 30 days after the expiration of the 1-year period.

b. A Class A mobile station authorized in this service may be used or operated anywhere in the United States subject to the provisions of paragraph (d) of this section: *Provided,* That when the area of operation is changed for a period exceeding 7 days, the following procedure shall be observed:

1. When the change of area of operations occurs inside the same Radio District, the Engineer in Charge of the Radio District involved and the Commission's office, Washington, D.C., 20554, shall be notified.

2. When the station is moved from one Radio District to another, the Engineers in Charge of the two Radio Districts involved and the Commission's office, Washington, D.C., 20554, shall be notified.

c. A Class C or Class D mobile station may be used or operated anywhere in the United States subject to the provisions of paragraph (d) of this section.

d. A mobile station authorized in this service may be used or operated on any vessel, aircraft, or vehicle of the United States: *Provided,* That when such vessel, aircraft, or vehicle is outside the territorial limits of the United States, the station, its operation, and its operator shall be subject to the governing provisions of any treaty concerning telecommunications to which the United States is a party, and when within the territorial limits of any foreign country, the station shall be subject also to such laws and regulations of that country as may be applicable.

§ 95.119   Control points, dispatch points, and remote control.

a. A control point is an operating position which is under the control and supervision of the licensee, at which a person immediately responsible for the proper operation of the transmitter is stationed, and at which adequate means are available to aurally monitor all transmissions and to render the transmitter inoperative. Each Class A base or fixed station shall be provided with a control point, the location of which will be specified in the license. The location of the control point must be the same as the transmitting equipment unless the application includes a request for a different location. Exception to the requirement for a control point may be made by the Commission upon specific request and justification therefor in the case of certain unattended Class A stations employing special emissions pursuant to § 95.47(e). Authority for such exception must be shown on the license.

b. A dispatch point is any position from which messages may be transmitted under the supervision of the person at a control point who is responsible for the proper operation of the transmitter. No authorization is required to install dispatch points.

c. Remote control of a Citizens radio station means the control of the transmitting equipment of that station from any place other than the location of the transmitting equipment, except that direct mechanical control or direct electrical control by wired connections of transmitting equipment from some other point on the same premises, craft, or vehicle shall not be considered remote control. A Class A base or fixed station may be authorized to be used or operated by remote control from another fixed location or from mobile units: *Provided,* That adequate means are available to enable the person using or operating the station to render the transmitting equipment inoperative from each remote control position should improper operation occur.

d. Operation of any Class C or Class D station by remote control is prohibited except remote control by wire upon specific authorization by the Commission when satisfactory need is shown.

§ 95.121 Civil defense communications.

A licensee of a station authorized under this part may use the licensed radio facilities for the transmission of messages relating to civil defense activities in connection with official tests or drills conducted by, or actual emergencies proclaimed by, the civil defense agency having jurisdiction over the area in which the station is located: *Provided,* That:

a. The operation of the radio station shall be on a voluntary basis.

b. [Reserved]

c. Such communications are conducted under the direction of civil defense authorities.

d. As soon as possible after the beginning of such use, the licensee shall send notice to the Commission in Washington, D.C., and to the Engineer in Charge of the Radio District in which the station is located, stating the nature of the communications being transmitted and the duration of the special use of the station. In addition, the Engineer in Charge shall be notified as soon as possible of any change in the nature of or termination of such use.

e. In the event such use is to be a series of pre-planned tests or drills of the same or similar nature which are scheduled in advance for specific times or at certain intervals of time, the licensee may send a single notice to the Commission in Washington, D.C., and to the Engineer in Charge of the Radio District in which the station is located, stating the nature of the communications to be transmitted, the duration of each such test, and the times scheduled for such use. Notice shall likewise be given in the event of any change in the nature of or termination of any such series of tests.

f. The Commission may, at any time, order the discontinuance of such special use of the authorized facilities.

SUBPART E—OPERATION OF CITIZENS RADIO STATIONS IN THE UNITED STATES BY CANADIANS

§ 95.131   Basis, purpose and scope.

a. The rules in this subpart are based on, and are applicable solely to the agreement (TIAS #6931) between the United States and Canada, effective July 24, 1970, which permits Canadian stations in the General Radio Service to be operated in the United States.

b. The purpose of this subpart is to implement the agreement (TIAS #6931) between the United States and Canada by prescribing rules under which a Canadian licensee in the General Radio Service may operate his station in the United States.

§ 95.133   Permit required.

Each Canadian licensee in the General Radio Service desiring to operate his radio station in the United States, under the provisions of the agreement (TIAS #6931), must obtain a permit for such operation from the Federal Communications Commission. A permit for such operation shall be issued only to a person holding a valid license in the General Radio Service issued by the appropriate Canadian governmental authority.

§ 95.135   Application for permit.

a. Application for a permit shall be made on FCC Form 410–B. Form 410–B may be obtained from the Commission's Washington, D.C., office or from any of the Commission's field offices. A separate application form shall be filed for each station or transmitter desired to be operated in the United States.

b. The application form shall be completed in full in English and signed by the applicant. The application must be filed by mail or in person with the Federal Communications Commission, Gettysburg, Pa. 17325, U.S.A. To allow sufficient time for processing, the application should be filed at least 60 days before the date on which the applicant desires to commence operation.

c. The Commission, at its discretion, may require the Canadian licensee to give evidence of his knowledge of the Commission's applicable rules and regulations. Also the Commission may require the applicant to furnish any additional information it deems necessary.

§ 95.137   Issuance of permit.

a. The Commission may issue a permit under such conditions, restrictions and terms as it deems appropriate.

b. Normally, a permit will be issued to expire 1 year after issuance but in no event after the expiration of the license issued to the Canadian licensee by his government.

c. If a change in any of the terms of a permit is desired, an application for modification of the permit is required. If operation beyond the expiration date of a permit is desired an application for renewal of the permit is required. Application for modification or for renewal of a permit shall be filed on FCC Form 410–B.

d. The Commission, in its discretion, may deny any application for a permit under this subpart. If an application is denied, the applicant will be notified by letter. The applicant may, within 30 days of the mailing of such letter, request the Commission to reconsider its action.

§ 95.139   Modification or cancellation of permit.

At any time the Commission may, in its discretion, modify or cancel any permit issued under this subpart. In this event, the permittee will be notified of the Commission's action by letter mailed to his mailing address in the United States and the permittee shall comply immediately. A permittee may, within 30 days of the mailing of such letter, request the Commission to reconsider its action. The filing of a request for reconsideration shall not stay the effectiveness of that action, but the Commission may stay its action on its own motion.

§ 95.141   Possession of permit.

The current permit issued by the Commission, or a

photocopy thereof, must be in the possession of the operator or attached to the transmitter. The license issued to the Canadian licensee by his government must also be in his possession while he is in the United States.

§ 95.143   Knowledge of rules required.

Each Canadian permittee, operating under this subpart, shall have read and understood this Part 95, Citizens Radio Service.

§ 95.145   Operating conditions.

a. The Canadian licensee may not under any circumstances begin operation until he has received a permit issued by the Commission.

b. Operation of station by a Canadian licensee under a permit issued by the Commission must comply with all of the following:

1. The provisions of this subpart and of Subparts A through D of this part.

2. Any further conditions specified on the permit issued by the Commission.

§ 95.147   Station identification.

The Canadian licensee authorized to operate his radio station in the United States under the provisions of this subpart shall identify his station by the call sign issued by the appropriate authority of the government of Canada followed by the station's geographical location in the United States as nearly as possible by city and state.

Thrilling, mind-expanding novels and stories by science fiction's most prestigious authors

The TEMPO Science Fiction Library

____12126 THE WEAPON MAKERS
A. E. Van Vogt ($1.25)
One man decides a monumental battle between The Weapon Shops and an entire empire. "One of the all-time greats!"—*Fantasy & Science Fiction*

____12127 PLANETS FOR SALE
A. E. Van Vogt and E. Mayne Hull ($1.25)
In a future where tycoons joust for control of a galaxy, the enigmatic Artur Blord, idealist, scoundrel, and financial wizard, fights for power and for love.

____12128 EIGHTEEN GREATEST SCIENCE FICTION STORIES Laurence M. Janifer, ed. ($1.50)
The greatest science fiction writers' own choice of the greatest science fiction stories ever written. With stories by Bradbury, Heinlein, Sturgeon, and 15 other masters.

____12129 VOYAGERS IN TIME
Robert Silverberg, ed. ($1.25)
A Hugo Award Winner's superb collection of twelve time travel stories by H. G. Wells, Bester, del Rey, among others.

____12130 MINDS UNLEASHED
Groff Conklin, ed. ($1.25)
The incredible powers of human intelligence are the theme of this fascinating anthology. A dozen stories by Clarke, Leinster, Tenn, Asimov, and other greats.

____12131 GREAT STORIES OF SPACE TRAVEL
Groff Conklin, ed. ($1.25)
The shores of space explored by eleven notables, including Vance, del Rey, Knight, and Clarke.